Myths and legends

DINAH STARKEY

TEACHER TIMESAVERS

Published by Scholastic Publications Ltd,
Villiers House,
Clarendon Avenue,
Leamington Spa,
Warwickshire CV32 5PR

© **1995 Scholastic Publications Ltd**
Text © 1995 Dinah Starkey

Author Dinah Starkey
Editor Jo Saxelby-Jennings
Assistant editor Joanne Boden
Series designer Joy White
Designer Tracey Ramsey
Illustrations Gay Galsworthy
Cover illustration Frances Lloyd
Cover photograph Martyn Chillmaid

Designed using Aldus Pagemaker
Processed by Pages Bureau, Leamington Spa
Artwork by Steve Williams Design, Leicester
Printed in Great Britain by Clays Ltd, Bungay, Suffolk

British Library Cataloguing-in-Publication Data
A catalogue record for this book is
available from the British Library.

ISBN 0-590-53194-8

Contents

Introduction

This book contains a collection of myths and legends from all over the world. They have been chosen, first and foremost, because they are good stories which appeal to a wide age range. In addition, they open windows into other times and other places and help children to think themselves into the minds of men and women who lived long ago and reflect their beliefs and values. For example, at the heart of the Ancient Egyptian rituals of mummification and burial, lies the story of 'Osiris'. This makes them particularly useful as a starting point for history topics.

Stories are useful for building historical skills. They help children to think about motivation (What made Pandora open the box, for example?), and the causes and consequences of people's actions. They provide practice in chronological sequencing and contribute to an understanding of change and of differences between past and present.

However, there are many versions of the past and, quite early on, children must learn to distinguish between fact and fiction. Myths and legends, with their formalised structure and bold characterisation, are helpful here. At the heart of many stories there is a core of historical fact. Older children can play historical detective games and look for clues to the truth in a story such as 'Theseus and the Minotaur', or the enduring legend of King Arthur. The story of 'Beowulf' could be combined with archaeological evidence from Sutton Hoo and information from secondary sources to build up a picture of life in Anglo-Saxon Britain.

Some of the myths in this book are very well-known. If possible, try to find a different telling of the story of 'Persephone', or 'Rama and Sita', or

compare the biblical Noah with 'Manu and the Flood', to allow the children to develop the concept of alternative versions of events. They must learn also that versions of an account may vary according to the teller. How might the tale of 'Thor goes fishing' have differed if it had been told by the frost giant, for example?

Ideas for developing a history topic through story are given on the planning grid on page 11.

The photocopiable sheets

The book is divided into five sections. The activity sheets, which accompany each story, offer ideas for developing historical skills, while suggestions for extension work are included in the teachers' notes. Since stories lend themselves to a cross-curricular approach, there are also suggested starting points for geography, RE, English and technology.

The stories could also provide stimuli for art and design, music, dance and drama. For example, the children's paintings of the Greek gods could be compared with versions by adults, while the legends of 'Rama and Sita' or 'The first fire' are ideal subjects for dance-drama and percussion composition.

How it all began

Creation myths are the earliest kind of history; reflecting people's first attempts to explain the past. Stories of 'The Flood', the creation of fire and explanations of why evil came into the world are universal. However, encourage the children to reflect on how local culture and living conditions have affected the telling of the stories. As well as discussing differences, it is important to emphasise the commonality of experience. This section offers many opportunities for RE work.

Special people

These are the men and women whose stories have been passed down through generations of oral tradition. Most of them are real people, although their stories are mythical. These stories help children to understand how history can be distorted by popular memory. Since these stories reflect the values of earlier times, women are under represented and you may wish to discuss some more of the heroic women who existed in real life, such as Boudicca and Grace Darling.

Special times

The stories in this section come from the Key Stage 2 history study areas of: Ancient Egypt; Ancient Greece; Romans, Anglo-Saxons and Vikings in Britain; Life in Tudor Times; The Aztecs; and Benin. They can be used to introduce or enrich a history topic and will help you to meet the National Curriculum requirement to teach history from a variety of different perspectives, and to introduce children to the ideas, attitudes and beliefs of people within particular periods.

Special days

These stories are particularly relevant to Key Stage 1 children, whose understanding of time is still immature. Temporal concepts are among the last to develop and many reception children have difficulty in visualising the passage of a day. We can help children to measure the passage of time by identifying the landmark events. Memories of a previous birthday or religious festival, and anticipation of the one to come, help the child to make sense of the cyclical nature of the year and to develop some notion of its span.

The stories in this section could slot into a class discussion or school assembly, or provide a stimulus for display, role-play or drama.

Special places

These stories will provide an insight into other countries and cultures, and all five continents are represented. You can use these stories to develop general cultural awareness or to enrich a study of a geographical area outside the UK.

About the author

Dinah Starkey is History Adviser for Wiltshire Education Authority. She read 'Dark Age History' at Somerville College, Oxford, and is the author of several collections of myths and legends. She has taught both infants and juniors and lectures on 'History in the Early Years' at Bath College of Higher Education.

How it all began

Persephone (Ancient Greece) This is one of the best known of all the Greek myths and there are many versions of it. Variations include: the god who informed Demeter of Persephone's kidnapper, the nature of the food Persephone ate in the Underworld, and the length of her stay there. Try to read another version of the story and discuss the differences. The Greek idea of the Underworld can be compared with that of the Babylonians, as described in the story of 'Gilgamesh' (pages 140–141).

The summer story Ask the children to retell the story to a friend. Let them choose their favourite scene to draw as part of a captioned wall frieze.

Sunny days This activity helps children to identify the landmark events of the year. They may wish to include birthdays and family events.

Simplify this sheet by suggesting celebrations for some of the empty boxes. For example: January – New Year's Day; February – St Valentine's Day, Chinese New Year; May – May Day; July – schools break up, Independence Day in USA; September – school starts again; October – Harvest Festival; November – Diwali, Bonfire Night; December – Christmas, Hanukah.

How Glooskap found Summer (Canada) Glooskap is a hero figure in the mythology of the north-eastern Canadian Indians. Like the Aztec god, Quetzalcoatl, he is the friend and teacher of his people and, like King Arthur, it is believed that he will return to the world in time of need.

Myths and mapwork In the Greek story, summer is seen as the normal state. It is only when Persephone is stolen that winter can enter the world. In the Canadian story, Glooskap has to go and find summer. Both treat winter as an enemy. Either story provides a good starting point for a topic about the causes of seasonal variations and their effects on everyday life.

The first fire (Australia) The discovery of fire features prominently in creation myths. The Greeks believed that Prometheus, the Titan, stole it from the gods and hid it in a hollow fennel stalk, while according to the Maoris, fire was the gift of the fire goddess to her grandson. The children could discuss why so many legends have survived and then try inventing one of their own.

Fire – help or harm? The discovery of fire was a turning point in the life of humankind. Early people used it as protection against other humans and animals, for hardening wooden tools and weapons, for smelting metal and baking clay pots, as well as for cooking food, keeping warm and providing light.

Manu and the Flood (India) Most early civilisations have a flood legend. Some scholars believe that these stories may reflect a genuine inundation of the Fertile Crescent, the area between the Tigris and Euphrates rivers. The story of Manu could be compared with the biblical account of 'Noah's Ark' (*Genesis* 6:9–9:17).

Ra the sun god (Ancient Egypt) The Ancient Egyptians believed that, by day, Ra travelled across the sky in a golden barque and that at night he sailed through the Underworld. The scarab beetle was his symbol because it rolls its ball of dung across the ground as Ra rolled the sun before him. The children could look for representations of the scarab in illustrations of Egyptian tomb paintings.

Gods and goddesses of Ancient Egypt The activity 'Up on Mount Olympus' (page 81) would provide a starting point for investigating the equivalent gods of Ancient Greece. *Answers*: goddess of war – Sekhmet; sun god – Ra; god of the Underworld – Osiris; goddess of love – Hathor; scribe of the gods – Thoth; guardian of the tomb – Anubis.

The first Incas (South America/Peru) The Incan empire stretched 4,000km (2,500 miles) along the west coast of South America, covering most of modern-day Peru, part of Ecuador and Bolivia, north-west Argentina and the greater part of Chile. The empire was at its height from 1438 (when the Incas conquered the area around the city of Cuzco in the Andes, making it their capital) until 1534 and the arrival of the Spanish conquistadores. The Incas worshipped many gods, each associated with some aspect of nature. Most important was Viracocha, the creator god, while the Incan kings believed they were descended from the sun god, Inti.

Inca picture quiz

Answers:
- The Incas lived in present-day Peru.
- The women are weaving cloth.
- The bridge is made of rope.
- The picture shows a llama. The Incas kept them for wool, milk and meat, and used them as pack animals.
- Atahualpa was imprisoned by Pizarro, who promised him his freedom in return for a room full of gold. The Indians collected the ransom, but Pizarro broke his promise and Atahualpa was executed.

How Sun and Moon got into the sky (West Africa) The children could use reference books to find out what houses in West Africa look like and how they are built. Why do houses in hot countries differ from those in temperate ones?

Story sequencing Limit the number of pictures to two or three for younger children. More able children could be asked to retell the story and compare their version with that of a friend.

In the beginning... In the Norse version of the creation story, the world was formed from the body of an ice giant called Ymir, while the Plains Indians believed it was shaped from sand and mud brought up from the primeval waters. How many versions of the creation story can you find?

Special people

The coming of Arthur (England) There is little hard evidence about Arthur. Chroniclers have associated him with the Battle of Badon, but they were writing long after the event. Many stories link him with the West Country and excavations at Cadbury in Somerset have revealed the remains of a hill-fort which was occupied when Arthur was said to have fought his battles.

Most modern historians now believe that this evidence, together with the persistent oral traditions, suggest that a war leader named Arthur or Artorius did exist, and may have been a cavalry leader who fought against the invading Saxons.

Will the real King Arthur please stand up? and **Arthur – true or false?** These sheets can be supplemented by 'Arthur's country' on page 48.

Robert the Bruce (Scotland) In 1290, Edward I of England invaded Scotland and claimed its throne. There followed 24 years of resistance, led first by William Wallace and later by Robert the Bruce, who eventually ruled Scotland from 1306 to 1329. The details of his early defeats and flight are historically accurate, but the episode of the spider remains unauthenticated.

Fact or point of view? Ask the children to offer statements about things they do at school, and then identify them as facts or points of view. For example, 'We go swimming on Mondays', 'My favourite subject is maths' and so on.

The two giants (Ireland) Finn MacCoul is one of Ireland's greatest folk heroes. This story shows him in a comic light, but there are many more in which he appears as an epic figure and a mighty war leader, gifted with magical powers.

Heroes' gallery Remind the children that heroines can be included in the picture line.

Johnny Appleseed John Chapman (1774–1845), known as 'Johnny Appleseed', planted orchards from Massachusetts to the Indiana border. The state of Ohio still has a 'Johnny Appleseed Week' in September. Like his contemporary, Davy Crockett, he attracted a trail of tall stories.

The cave of the sleepers (Wales) Like King Arthur, other heroes are reputed to lie sleeping until the time of their country's greatest need.

They include: Owen Glendower, William Wallace, Francis Drake and Charlemagne. Another version of this story sites the cave as being near Alderney Edge in Cheshire.

Arthur's country Few Arthurian place-names and stories occur in the east of Britain, which was most heavily colonised by the Saxons.

Robin Hood (England) Although stories about Robin Hood have been popular for centuries, there is little real evidence that he ever existed. The oldest ballads about him go back to the 1400s, and we know that he was a well-loved figure at the time of Chaucer.

In olden days... As an extension activity, brainstorm about life in the time of Robin Hood and then about life in, say, Victorian times. This kind of activity develops understanding of differences between times in the past.

Dick Whittington (England) Sir Richard Whittington was the son of Sir William Whittington of Pauntley, and became the wealthiest merchant in London. On several occasions he loaned large sums of money to King Richard II. He died in 1423, leaving all his great fortune for charity. The cat has been explained either as a kind of ship whose cargo brought him profit, or as a corruption of the French word *'achat'* meaning 'to purchase'.

The real Dick Whittington Other nursery rhymes describing historical events include 'Mary, Mary, quite contrary' and 'Little Jack Horner'. The first refers to the Catholic queen, Mary Tudor, with her silver altar bells. The second remembers Sir John Horner, steward to Glastonbury Abbey. The manor of Mells was the 'plum' which he 'pulled out' during the Dissolution. *Answers*: Old King Cole; Ring-a-ring o' roses; London Bridge is falling down; The grand old Duke of York.

Drake's cannon-ball (Tudors) The great Elizabethan seaman, Francis Drake (1540–1596), left England in 1577 with a fleet of five ships to sail around the world. The journey took three years and, on his return, he was knighted on the deck of his flagship, *The Golden Hind*, at the queen's command.

Famous Elizabethans Look at contemporary portraits of Drake and Raleigh (reproduced in many information books). What differences do the children notice? How do we know they were rich and powerful men?

The legendary Drake
Answers: the following statements are legends – He lies sleeping in his hammock...; He used magic to call up a wind; He was playing bowls when the Armada came.

My hero! Every nation has its folk heroes. For example, Welsh children might focus on Owen Glendower, the great freedom fighter, whose stand against the English in 1400 is legendary. Like Finn MacCoul, in Ireland, he was believed to be a magician with power over the weather.

Peoples from the past The dates have been rounded for ease of handling. Some of them are approximate and reflect the best guess of historians in the field. *Answers*: Egyptians – burial of Tutankhamen; Greeks – Battle of Salamis; Romans – occupation of Britain; Anglo-Saxons – King Alfred; Vikings – Leif Ericsson; Aztecs – completion of Tenochtitlan.

Special times

Thor goes fishing (Vikings) Thor was famous for his strength, his courage and his huge appetite. More brawn than brain, he was a great favourite of the Viking warriors and many Viking graves contain a hammer-shaped amulet.

Viking gods and goddesses
Answers: Monday – moon day; Tuesday – Tew or Tyr's day; Wednesday – Woden's day; Thursday – Thor's day; Friday – Freya or Frigga's day; Saturday – Saturn's day; Sunday – sun day.

World Serpent puzzle
Answers: special weapon – stone hammer which returned to his hand; special weather – thunder and lightning; day of the week – Thursday; names of (two) more gods – Odin, Loki, Baldur, Tyr, Freya (see page 65 for more information); home of the gods – Asgard.

Plumed Serpent When the Spanish first arrived in the sixteenth century, pale skinned and shining in their unfamiliar armour, some Aztecs took them for Quetzalcoatl and his followers. For a vital few days the Aztecs were undecided whether to attack or welcome the newcomers; a key factor in the Spanish conquest of Mexico.

Picture writing The Aztecs recorded important events and rituals as a series of pictures, a little like a very detailed comic strip. They were drawn on long pieces of bark, folded to make a zigzag book. The children can easily copy this format.

The oba of Benin (The Benin civilisation) Benin is a country on the west coast of Africa, noted for its superb sculptures and bronze work, and for a rich oral tradition. In the past, it was a great trading nation and was at the height of its prosperity during the sixteenth century. Benin is included in the list of non-European civilisations which form part of the Key Stage 2 Programme of Study for history.

Days to remember
Answers:
• Bonfire Night (5 November) commemorates Guy Fawkes' unsuccessful attempt to blow up the Houses of Parliament;

• Poppy Day (11 November) is the anniversary of the Armistice after World War I;
• Oak Apple Day (29 May) celebrates the restoration of Charles I and remembers him hiding from the Roundheads in an oak tree;
• Burns' Night (25 January) is the birthday of the Scottish poet Robert Burns and is celebrated in Scotland with haggis and Scotch whisky;
• D-Day (6 June) was the day when the Allies landed in France at the end of World War II.

Beowulf (Saxons) This story is the sole survivor of a body of Anglo-Saxon epics. It was originally passed on by word of mouth. Scholars believe it was written down in the eighth century, about 100 years before the time of King Alfred.

In the great hall To develop this worksheet into a drama, ask the children to take on the roles of the Saxon villagers in the great hall, listening to the story of 'Beowulf' at the end of a hard day.

Riddles and sagas *Answer*: a book.

Romulus and Remus The traditional date of the foundation of Rome is 753 BC and archeological evidence confirms that villages were developed on the seven hills overlooking the River Tiber at around that time.

Where to build Rome? *Answer*: site C.

Pandora's box (Ancient Greece) Compare this Greek myth with the Jewish story of Adam and Eve. As a follow-up, ask the children to name some of the bad things in the world today and compare them with the troubles of Ancient Greece. Many, such as war or famine are common to both cultures. Others, such as slavery or pollution, are specific to individual cultures. You may wish to discuss with older children the justice of attributing them to a single person or group. This may lead on to the concept of 'the scapegoat'.

Up on Mount Olympus
Answers:
- Zeus, the king of the gods, gave Pandora life;
- Athene wove beautiful clothes for her;
- Aphrodite gave her beauty;
- Apollo gave her the gift of music;
- Poseidon gave her courage.

Osiris (Ancient Egypt) The Ancient Egyptians believed that Pharaoh, when he died, became the embodiment of Osiris and his living successor became Osiris' son, Horus. Thus, tomb paintings often include representations of Osiris, who is shown as a mummy-like figure, dressed all in white and wearing the sacred beard. The children could be encouraged to look for examples in reference books.

The 40 judges The Ancient Egyptians compiled a *Book of the Dead* to guide the soul through the Underworld. This was a collection of magical spells and charms to help during the many tests. The children might like to make up their own *Book of the Dead*, illustrated with hieroglyphs.

Theseus and the Minotaur (Ancient Greece) and **Left Behind!** There are several explanations as to why Theseus abandoned Ariadne: that he simply forgot her; that the god Dionysos met her and took her to be his priestess; or that she conceived a hatred for Theseus because, on escaping from Crete, he killed her father.

Was there really a King Minos? Archeological evidence suggests that there was a flourishing civilisation on Crete thousands of years before the rise of classical Greece and that the Minoans practised some kind of bull worship. This may have given rise to the legend of the Minotaur.

Jason and the Argonauts (Ancient Greece) Until recent times, the tribesmen of Colchis in Turkey gathered gold by suspending sheepskins in the gold-bearing streams of the mountainous regions. It is possible that this story reflects some early raid by Greek adventurers.

Evidence of the past This worksheet makes a good starting point for an investigation into Greek ships. Several classical illustrations have survived. Encourage the children to look at the evidence carefully and to discuss ways in which it conflicts or agrees.

Comparing your story The children will find that they produce different versions of a shared story. This shows the way in which different viewpoints lead to varying interpretations of the past.

Special days

Prince Siddhartha (Wesak) Gautama Siddhartha (*c.* 560 BC – 483 BC) was born in India. After his death, he was named the 'Buddha' or the 'Enlightened One'. Wesak, which falls in the summer, is celebrated by Therevada Buddhists.

Perfect peace You may like to discuss the rules laid down by other religious leaders, such as Jesus, Guru Nanak or Muhammad.

Japanese New Year (New Year) This Shinto story dates back to the eighth century. Shinto is still the official religion of Japan and the sun goddess, Amateresu, is revered as a member of the Shinto pantheon.

New Year customs
Answers (clockwise):
- the Scots (or British) sing 'Auld lang syne';
- the Chinese celebrate with a lion dance;
- the Japanese make rope decorations;
- people in Hindu and Sikh countries (for example, India or Pakistan) regard Diwali as the start of the new year;
- some English (or British) people gather in Trafalgar Square, London, to see in New Year.

St George and the dragon (St George's Day) St George is believed to have been a Roman officer who was martyred in Palestine (*c.* AD 300). He was the patron saint of the Crusaders, and was established as patron saint of England by Edward III.

A calendar of special days Some festivals are 'moveable', for example Chinese New Year and Eid-ul-Fitr. Chinese New Year falls in February or March, while Eid-ul-Fitr is calculated by the moon phases and so progresses around the calendar, being about 11 days earlier each year.

St Patrick and the snakes (St Patrick's day) St Patrick's symbol is the three-leaved shamrock which he used to illustrate the Christian concept of three persons in one God: the Trinity of the Father, Son and Holy Spirit.

The Union Jack *Answer*: the missing flag is the 'Red Dragon of Wales'.

Rama and Sita (Diwali) This story is from the Sanskrit epic, the *Ramayana*. Rama and Sita are Hindu gods and are still worshipped.

Storytelling Once the children have completed this sheet, ask them to retell the story through drawing, shadow puppetry, drama or music.

Fire symbols The name Diwali means 'a row of lights'. It is a moveable feast which is celebrated in the autumn by both Sikhs and Hindus and it marks the beginning of the new year.
Answers (from left to right, top row): Diwali, Bonfire Night, Easter, Advent; (bottom row) Chinese New Year, Birthdays, Hanukah.

The marathon The battle of Marathon took place in 490 BC.

The Olympic games Extend this activity by asking the children how we know about the sports practised in the Ancient Greek games? What evidence is left?

St Nicholas (Christmas) St Nicholas was Bishop of Myra, in Turkey, in the early fourth century. He is patron saint of Russia and of pawnbrokers.

La Befana (Twelfth Night) This Italian story provides a good starting point for a topic on Christmas in other lands.

The twelve days of Christmas Christmas was developed from the Roman feast of 'Saturnalia'. 6 January is the Christian 'Feast of the Epiphany', when the wise men offered their gifts to the Holy Family. In the old days, a 'Bean King' was chosen by baking a cake containing a single bean. Whoever got the slice of cake with the bean became the 'king', leading his court in fancy-dress fun and games.

Christmas-time traditions This sheet illustrates popular customs from throughout the festive season: from Advent carol singers to the Twelfth Night tradition of 'La Befana'. The first nativity scene was organised by St Francis of Assisi, using live characters, and the tradition of the crib figures was popularised in France.

Special places

The Pied Piper of Hamelin (Hamelin/Germany) Robert Browning made this legend famous in his poem of that name. The event originally comes from Westphalia, in Germany, and is traditionally dated as 1284. In Browning's version, the children vanished into the mountain, but another variant states that they were led to Transylvania where they formed a German colony. The legend has its roots in the true story of the 'Children's crusade'.

Deep in thought Considering a story from different points of view prepares children for the idea that an historical account may be biased by the viewpoint of its author.

Sindbad the sailor (Baghdad/Arabian) This legendary figure is one of the heroes of *The Arabian Nights*. He was a wealthy citizen of Baghdad and made seven voyages and had many adventures.

Famous sailors *Answers*: Christopher Columbus (?1451–1506) crossed the Atlantic in 1492 and claimed the Americas for Spain; Odysseus is the hero of Homer's *Odyssey*; Francis Drake, explorer and pirate, (1540–1596) was the first Englishman to circumnavigate the world; Long John Silver appears in R.L. Stevenson's *Treasure Island*; Anne Bonny was a lady pirate in the early eighteenth century; and James Cook (1728–1779) was the first European to reach Australia.

Rip Van Winkle (Catskill Mountains/USA) This story, which was retold by Washington Iriving, is based on a German or Dutch legend.

Newfangled machines Extend this activity by asking the children to find out approximately when these machines first came into service.

Anansi looks for a wife (Africa) Anansi stories come from the west coast of Africa and from the West Indies. Anansi is both hero and trickster and in some stories possesses magical powers.

The jackdaw of Rheims (Rheims/France) This story featured in the *Ingoldsby Legends* (1840) published by the Reverend Richard Barham.

Good table manners There is considerable emphasis on the importance of having clean hands in medieval books of manners because diners used their fingers to pick morsels out of a common pot.

Black duck's children (Australia) The Australian Aboriginies believe that, in the very beginning, there was a period which they call the 'Dreamtime' when the world and everything in it first took shape.

Animal wordsearch
Answers:

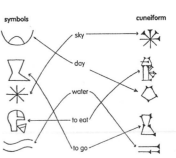

Gilgamesh (Mesopotamia) This legend was first written down about 2000 BC. It was inscribed on clay tablets, found in the library of Asur-bani-pal, king of Assyria. Scholars think the story itself is much earlier and may date from 3000 BC.

Beginning to write
Answers – the Babylonian symbols were:
mountain =   ; to be furious =

History through story: An example planning grid

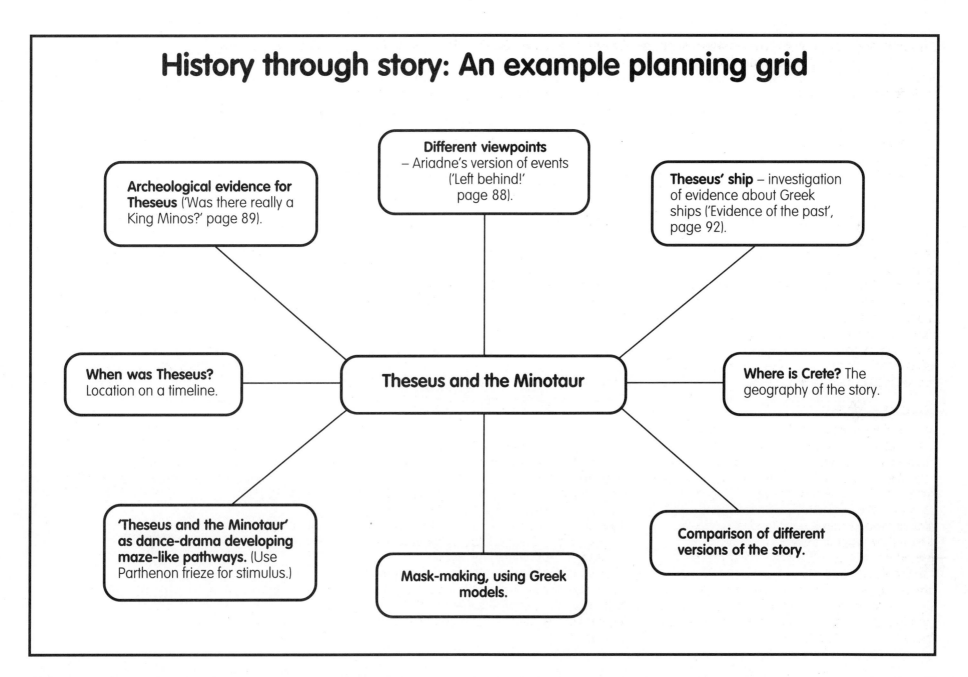

Different viewpoints – Ariadne's version of events ('Left behind!' page 88).

Archeological evidence for Theseus ('Was there really a King Minos?' page 89).

Theseus' ship – investigation of evidence about Greek ships ('Evidence of the past', page 92).

When was Theseus? Location on a timeline.

Theseus and the Minotaur

Where is Crete? The geography of the story.

'Theseus and the Minotaur' as dance-drama developing maze-like pathways. (Use Parthenon frieze for stimulus.)

Mask-making, using Greek models.

Comparison of different versions of the story.

Thematic Index

Persephone

This is a Greek story which explains how winter came to the world.

Demeter searched the world from end to end, but she could not find her daughter. She left the orchards and gardens untended and nothing could grow or flower. The sky grew dark and storms lashed the fields. Winter had come into the world.

At last Helios, the sun god, told her that Hades had stolen her daughter. So Demeter went to Zeus, the king of the gods, and demanded his help in getting back Persephone. Zeus, seeing the ruined crops and dying gardens everywhere, agreed to do what he could.

The goddess of things which grow was called Demeter. She sent rain to swell the corn and sun to ripen the apples. She brought luck to the planting and luck to the harvest.

Demeter had one daughter called Persephone, whom she loved dearly. However, Hades, the god of the Underworld, saw Persephone and wanted her for his wife. So he carried her off to his cold kingdom underground and there he kept her prisoner.

Zeus crossed the River Styx and descended to the Underworld to speak to his brother, Hades. He found him sitting on a great throne, and there was Persephone beside him, crowned with gold, but as pale and silent as a ghost.

Name _____

Zeus commanded Hades to return Persephone to her mother. He had taken her against her own wishes and she must be allowed to go free. This was the law and Hades had to agree, but his kingdom had another law of its own. Whoever ate the food of the dead belonged to the Underworld, and Persephone had eaten six pomegranate seeds.

But Zeus was king of the gods and stronger even than death. He struck a bargain with Hades. For half the year, Persephone was to go free and could return to her mother. However, the other half of the year she must spend in the kingdom of the dead, because she had eaten the pomegranate seeds.

So that's how winter came into the world. For when Persephone returns to Hades, Demeter weeps and turns her face away from the world. Then the crops stop growing and the flowers wither. But when the six months are over and her daughter comes back, Demeter rejoices and all the world is green again.

The summer story

❖ Cut out the pictures below and arrange them in the right order.

❖ Write a sentence to go with each picture.

_____
_____
_____

_____
_____
_____

_____
_____
_____

_____
_____
_____

Persephone

Name _____

Sunny days

❖ Draw a picture for each month.

❖ Draw the sun in the pictures of the months when you think
Persephone is allowed to leave the Underworld and return to her mother.

January	February	March	April
May	June	July	August
September	October	November	December

How Glooskap found Summer

This story comes from the Canadian Indians.

Long, long ago there lived a great magician called Glooskap. He was the chief of his tribe and he ruled them well. Then, one day, Winter entered his kingdom. Winter was an old giant who came from the far north and he was stronger than Glooskap and all his tribe put together.

Winter breathed on the land and it grew very cold. The crops died, the ground froze and the deep snow covered the grasslands. Glooskap's people began to die.

Glooskap set out over the snow to look for Winter. He found him in a cave made from ice and they fought together, but Winter defeated Glooskap and cast him into a deep sleep. He slept like a bear for six months, but at the end of it he awoke, for even Winter could not kill him. He left the ice cave and went looking for something stronger than Winter.

He rode on the back of a whale far across the sea until he came to a land of flowers where the winds were soft and the days were long and the birds sang in every tree. The queen of the land was called Summer, and she was as beautiful as the morning.

Glooskap asked Summer to go with him, but she would not leave her own country. So he captured her by a trick and carried her off.

Together they travelled for many days and nights until they reached Glooskap's kingdom.

Canada

He found it still and silent. Everyone lay asleep under the snow, except for old Winter in his ice cave in the mountains.

Then Winter fought with Summer and Summer was strongest. She broke Winter's spell and drove him back into the far north. Winter wept bitter tears at his defeat and Summer, seeing this, was sorry. She promised that the far north should always be his and that she would never come there.

Also, she agreed that for six months of every year he should rule in Glooskap's kingdom, but at the end of that time, he must give way to her.

Winter accepted these terms and that is why Summer never comes to the far north and ice and snow remain there all year round. However, in Glooskap's country, although it is cold for six months of the year, sooner or later Summer returns to drive the cold away.

Name _____

Myths and mapwork

✿ Read 'How Glooskap found Summer' and 'Persephone'. Both these stories explain how winter and summer came into the world.

Use an atlas to help you to do the following activities.

✿ Look for Canada and Greece on a map and shade them in below.

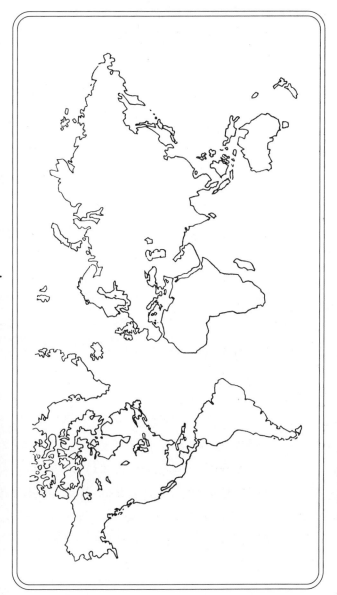

✿ Find out all you can about the weather in Canada and the weather in Greece and write two short descriptions below.

Canada

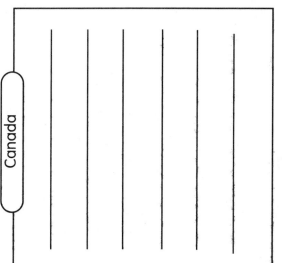

Greece

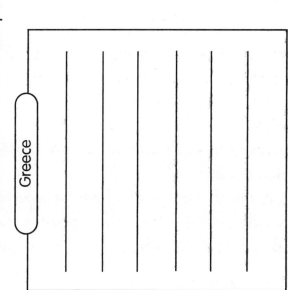

✿ Can you explain the similarities and differences between the stories? Use the information you have found out to help you.

Australia

The first fire

This is a story from Australia.

Long ago, when the world had just begun, there was no fire and everyone ate their food raw. Rat and Crane were the first to discover fire. They trapped it in a pot and used it to cook their food, but they kept the secret to themselves for fear that the other animals might steal it.

Soon all the other animals knew that Rat and Crane did something special to their food which made it smell and taste delicious, but it was done out of sight and nobody could find out what it was.

One day, Night Owl and Parrot followed Rat and Crane. They perched in a high tree and saw the pair take fire out of the pot, feed it with twigs, and cook some fish until it sizzled. Then Night Owl and Parrot returned to tell the other animals.

They all wanted fire, but they knew that Rat and Crane wouldn't share it, so they decided to steal it. They held a big party, called a corrobboree[1], and they invited Rat and Crane to come. Hawk was to pretend he'd hurt himself and lie close by them. His job was to watch and wait until he saw his chance to steal the pot.

It was a very big corrobboree. Tribes came from far and wide. Rat and Crane arrived carrying the fire pot and were given seats of honour. Hawk lay down beside them and kept very still.

1. 'Corrobboree' is an Aboriginal word meaning 'a night dance'.

One by one the tribes got up to dance. Rat watched, with her hand on the fire basket. But the night was long and the dancing was exciting. Her hand slipped and Hawk crept forward.

The parrots began to dance. They bowed and bobbed, faster and faster until Rat could not keep from laughing. She laughed so hard that she fell over backwards and Hawk saw his chance. He snatched up the fire pot, cut it open and pulled out the firestick which smouldered inside. Rat and Crane cried out and tried to stop him, but it was too late. Hawk was running, faster than they could follow. As he ran, he set fire to bushes and trees until there was a long trail of flame around the dancing place and Rat and Crane saw that they had lost their secret for ever.

So, they gave up the chase and, from that day on, fire belonged to everyone.

The first fire

Fire – help or harm?

♣ Was the discovery of fire a good thing or a bad thing?

♣ Think of some times when we use fire to **help** us and list them below.

♣ Think of some times when fire can **harm** us and list them below.

Manu and the Flood

This story comes from India.

There was once a holy man called Manu who lived on the banks of the River Ganges. One day, as he was praying, he heard a tiny voice calling to him.

'Manu!' said the voice. 'Help me, for it is the duty of a holy man to protect the weak.'

The voice came from the water. Manu looked down and saw a tiny fish.

'Help me,' it said. 'Put me in a jar and keep me safe, and in return I will help you. A great flood is coming and everyone will be drowned, but if you do as I say you can escape.'

Manu thought there was little that a tiny fish could do to help him, but, out of kindness, he did as he was asked. He put the fish in a jar made of clay and fed it every day, and it grew wonderfully. Soon it was too big for the jar. So Manu dug a pond outside, but the fish grew too big for the pond. It had reached the size of a dolphin when it said, 'The time of the flood is coming fast and I must leave you. Take me back to the River Ganges and then build yourself a boat. Put in seeds of every kind of plant and a long, strong rope. When the rain comes I will return and help you as I promised. You will know me by the horn on my head.'

Then Manu knew that this was no ordinary fish, but the Hindu god Vishnu, the preserver, who had come to warn him and he made haste to obey. He built a boat and stocked it with seeds from every plant in the world. Then he plaited a long rope. No sooner had he finished than the rains began.

It rained and rained until the whole world was covered with water and every rooftop was drowned. Manu's boat was lifted high above the hills

India

to drift on the waters. The rains drummed down and the wild winds blew and Manu grew frightened that he would be shipwrecked. But just as the waves seemed certain to swallow him, he saw a huge fish swimming towards him. It had a horn on its head and Manu knew that it was Lord Vishnu come to save him. So he threw his rope over the horn and the fish followed him to safety.

After many days more, the boat landed on a mountain peak high in the Himalayas and Manu returned to dry land again. He was the only person in the whole world to survive the flood, thanks to the god Vishnu.

Manu planted his seeds and made new gardens and he fathered another race to bring life to the world again. The children of Manu have remembered Vishnu for ever after and give thanks to him because he delivered them from the flood.

Manu's boat

✤ How many different plants can you think of?

✤ Draw them in Manu's boat and write their names beside them.

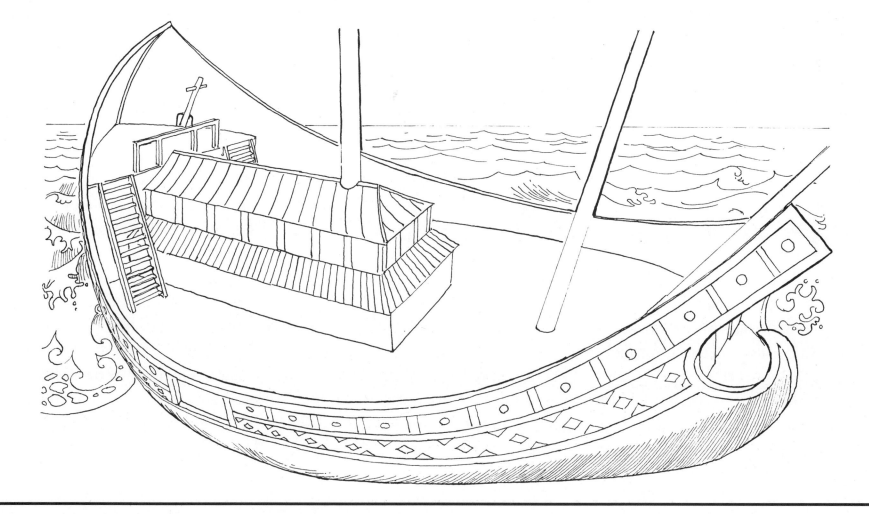

Ra the sun god

In the beginning, before the world began, there was water and, floating on the water, was a lotus flower. At night, the petals of the lotus opened and within them was the sun god, Ra.

Whatever Ra thought of came into being. Ra thought of wind and there was wind. He thought of rain and there was rain. He thought of the Earth and he named it Geb, or Egypt. He made the sky to arch over Egypt and the River Nile to flow through it. Then he made plants and birds and fish to live in his land and last of all he made men and women.

Ra became a man and ruled over Egypt. He was the first Pharaoh and his rule lasted for a thousand years. But he grew old and his people turned against him. They began to disobey his laws and worship other gods. So Ra made Sekhmet, the destroyer. He made her in the shape of a lioness and she fed on human blood. She hunted down the evildoers who had angered Ra and killed them, but when they were all gone, Sekhmet was still hungry and she turned on the good people too. She killed and killed until the River Nile was choked with bodies and the people of Egypt, in their terror, cried to Ra for help.

Ra set all his servants to work brewing strong beer. He ordered them to bring him red dye and he mixed this into the beer so that it looked like blood. At night, when it was dark, his servants carried the beer, jar after jar of it, to the place where Sekhmet slept and left it at her door.

Sekhmet awoke hungry for blood. She took the first jar and drained it. She drank the next and the next until she had emptied every one. The strong beer went to her head and she fell fast asleep. Then Ra came to her and spoke to her in a dream.

'Peace, Sekhmet,' he said. 'You have had your fill of blood and now I will change both your name and your nature. From henceforth you shall be called Hathor, and men will love you as much as they once feared you.'

So Sekhmet, the destroyer, became Hathor, the goddess of love, and the people of Egypt, who had learned their lesson, took care never to offend Ra, the sun god, again.

Name _____

Gods and goddesses of Ancient Egypt

❖ Read the clues and see if you can choose the correct name for each of these gods and goddesses from the list below. Use reference books to help you.

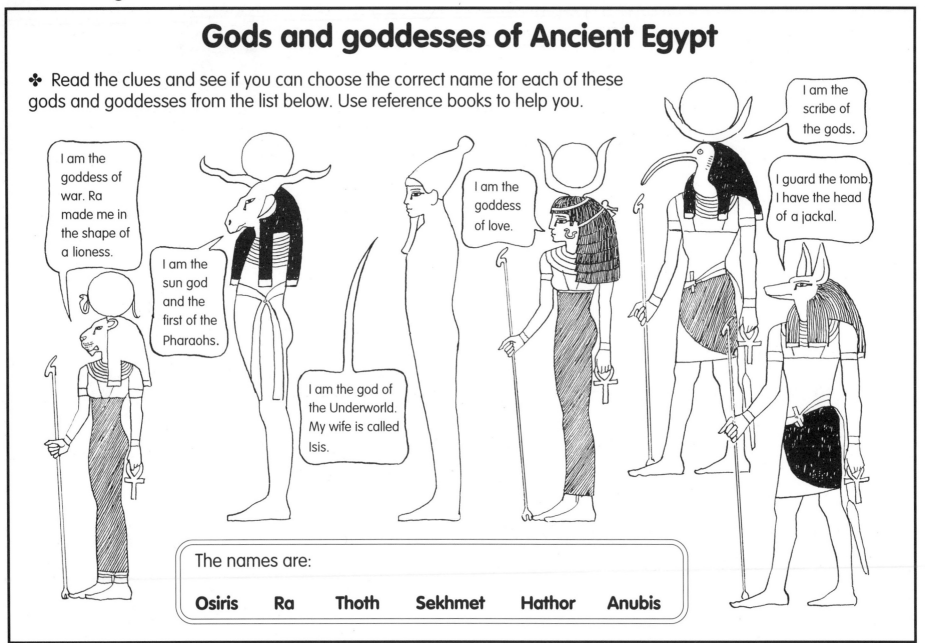

I am the goddess of war. Ra made me in the shape of a lioness.

I am the sun god and the first of the Pharaohs.

I am the god of the Underworld. My wife is called Isis.

I am the goddess of love.

I am the scribe of the gods.

I guard the tomb. I have the head of a jackal.

The names are:

Osiris   Ra   Thoth   Sekhmet   Hathor   Anubis

 # The first Incas

The first men lived like animals. They had no clothes and no fire. They lived in caves and ate roots and berries.

The sun god, Inti, took pity on them and sent his son, Ayar Manco, and daughter, Mama Oello, down to Earth to teach them how to cook and weave and farm the land.

The sun god's children travelled through the Andes mountains until they came to a place where they could settle. They built a city and they called it Cuzco. First they made a great temple to their father, the sun. But the wind in the mountains was so strong that it snatched away the blocks of stone they set up for the walls, and tore down the columns of the temple as fast as they were raised.

The sun god's children caught the wind. They shut it up in the pen where they kept the llamas[1]. The wind howled and beat against the door, but it could find no escape.

The temple was nearly finished when another of the sun's children, Ucho, came up from the lowlands where he lived.

'Brother,' he said. 'What is this creature you have trapped in your llama pen? I can hear it howling all the way to the plains.'

'It's the wind,' said his sister. 'We have shut it up because it stops us from building our temple.'

1. Llamas are animals that live in the high mountains.

Ucho was very angry. 'The wind is my friend,' he said. 'I forbid you to keep him prisoner. Tonight, at sunset, I will return and set him free.'

Nobody spoke. They all knew the city would never be finished by sunset. When Ucho had gone, Ayar Manco and Mama Oello called their strongest servant and told him to come with them to the top of the mountain.

They waited until their father, the sun, went by and they caught him and anchored him to a huge rock. He could not travel on to reach his setting place and his children had time to finish the city.

As soon as the last stone was in place they released first the sun and then the wind. Ayar Manco and Mama Oello married and they became the first Incas, the rulers of Peru. For many, many years they lived in the city of Cuzco which they had built on the roof of the world.

Inca picture quiz

Use reference books to help you with this quiz.

❧ Where did the Incas live?

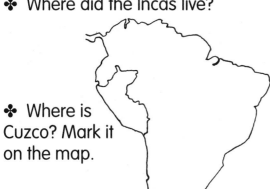

❧ Where is Cuzco? Mark it on the map.

❧ These Inca women are making something. Can you find out what it is?

This is called a 'quipu'. The Incas used it for counting.

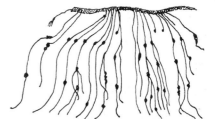

❧ See if you can find out more about it.

❧ What is this bridge made from?

❧ What is this animal?
❧ What did the Incas use it for?

This is Atahualpa, the last Inca king.
❧ Find out what happened to him.

West Africa

How Sun and Moon got into the sky

Long, long ago when the world was young, Sun and Moon lived in a house in a valley. Sun's best friend was Water, and Sun often went to visit him. One day, Sun said, 'It isn't fair. I visit you, but you never visit me. You must come to my house.'

'I'm very big,' said Water. 'I don't think I'll fit in your house.'

'Then I'll build a bigger one,' said Sun, and he set to work at once. He and Moon built the biggest house in the world and when it was finished, Sun said to Moon, 'Now I shall invite Water to visit us.'

Moon said, 'Are you sure there'll be room?'

'Quite sure,' said Sun, and off he went.

Next day, Sun and Moon stood at the doorway of their fine new house watching for Water. Moon was unhappy. She said, 'He won't fit in. We should have made it bigger.'

At that moment, the first little bit of Water came trickling round the corner. He rolled into the house and began to fill up the corner and wash against the walls. Sun and Moon climbed on to stools.

'We should have made it bigger,' said Moon again.

Still Water came. He poured into all the rooms and drove Sun and Moon out on to the roof.

'We should have made it bigger,' said Moon as Water lifted them off the roof and pushed them up into the sky. Sun and Moon found themselves floating in space. Below them they could see nothing but Water! The house, the valley and the whole land had gone.

'Maybe you're right,' said Sun. 'We should have made it bigger.'

But they never had another chance, and Sun and Moon have stayed up in the sky to this day.

Story sequencing

❖ Cut out the pictures below.

❖ Can you put the story in the right order?

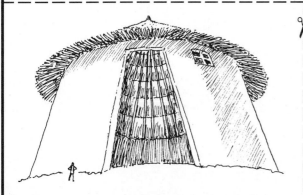

Sun and Moon built a house. It was the biggest house in the world.

Sun said, 'I always visit you, Water. You must come and visit me for a change.'

Sun and Moon looked down from the sky. There was Water everywhere.

Water began to pour into the house.

Once upon a time, Sun and Moon lived on Earth in a house in a valley.

Sun and Moon climbed up on to the roof.

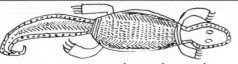

In the beginning...

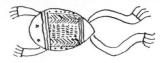

There are many stories about how the world began.

The Chinese say it started with an egg.

The egg cracked open and out came a giant who made the mountains.

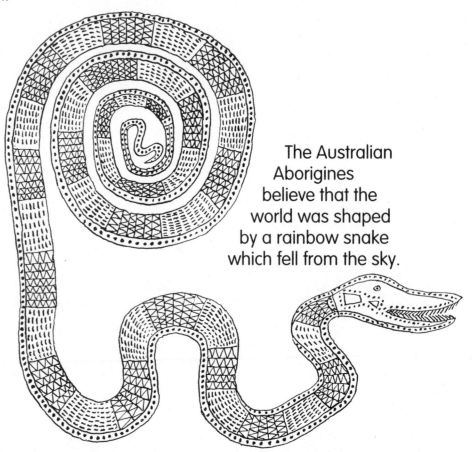

The Australian Aborigines believe that the world was shaped by a rainbow snake which fell from the sky.

❖ Find another story about how the world began. Retell it in your own words and draw a picture of what happened.

The coming of Arthur

There was once a king of England called Uther Pendragon who had a baby son, Arthur. One day, Uther sent for all the lords and magicians of his court and said, 'My life is near its end and very soon I will die. You must all promise to make my little son, Arthur, king after me.'

All the lords promised, but Uther was not satisfied. He feared that somebody might kill the baby and take the throne. So he said to his chief magician, Merlin, 'Hide Arthur for me, Merlin. Keep him safe until he is grown up and then he will return to rule the land.'

So Merlin magicked Arthur away to the castle of Sir Ector, who lived in the wild forest and very soon after, Uther Pendragon died.

As soon as he was gone, the lords forgot their promise. Everybody wanted to be king and soon the whole country was at war as lord fought with lord for the crown. All the time, Arthur was growing up, safe and hidden in the wild forest.

Now, there was a great block of stone in a churchyard in London, with a sword thrust through it with writing on it. The writing said: 'Whoever can draw this sword from the stone is true king of England.'

All the lords in London tried to pull the sword from the stone, but they couldn't. It was stuck tight.

There it stayed until one New Year's Day when Arthur was 16 years old. Sir Ector came to London with Arthur and his own son, Sir Kay, to join with other knights in feasting, riding and swordplay.

They all set off, but when they arrived at the meeting place, Sir Kay found that he had left his sword behind. Arthur was sent back for it and, as he hurried through the streets, he came to the churchyard where the magic sword stood in the stone. He didn't know the story and he thought that he would borrow the sword for Kay.

It was very quiet in the churchyard for everyone had gone to the feasting. Arthur was in too much of a hurry to read the writing. He took the sword by its hilt, pulled it out and carried it back to Sir Kay.

When the knights saw the sword they remembered the promise they had made to Uther Pendragon and they knew that this was Uther's son. They kneeled before him and accepted him as king. He was crowned that very day and he became one of the most famous kings ever known.

As for Sir Kay, he remained Arthur's faithful friend for as long as they lived.

Will the real King Arthur please stand up?

People believe Arthur must have existed because there are so many stories about him. They think he may have lived in AD 500, just after the Romans left Britain. However, evidence is hard to find. Here is some of it. See what you think.

AD 550 A monk wrote:

Artor fought for 3 days at the battle of Badon

BUT: does Artor mean Arthur?

AD 800 Another monk wrote:

Arthur was war leader of the Britons

BUT: he was writing 300 years later.

1190 Monks at Glastonbury dug up a coffin. They **said** it held the skeleton of King Arthur. **BUT:** the bones vanished and other people said it was a fake.

1970 Archaeologists dug up a hill in Somerset called Arthur's Palace. They found traces of a fort dating back to AD 500. **BUT:** they found nothing with Arthur's name on it.

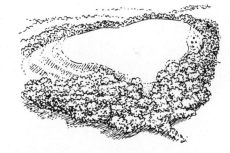

ALL OVER BRITAIN THERE ARE PLACES NAMED AFTER KING ARTHUR.

♣ Look at the evidence and talk about it with a friend.
♣ Make a list of evidence for Arthur being real and a list of evidence against.

Arthur – true or false?

♣ Do you think that the story of King Arthur is a true story or a made-up one?

♣ Make a list of the parts which might be true.

♣ Make a list of the parts which you think are made up.

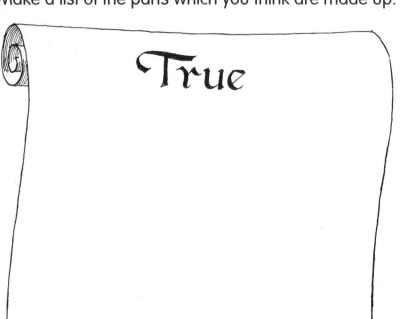

Robert the Bruce

Every country has its own heroes. One of the heroes of Scotland is Robert the Bruce. He lived nearly 700 years ago and the Scots remember him because he fought to make his country free. This is what happened.

In those days Scotland and England were two different kingdoms. Scotland was ruled by a Scottish king and England by an English king.

But the Scottish king died, and the English king, Edward I, saw his chance to take over Scotland. He marched armies into Scotland and told the Scottish people that they had to obey him and give him money because he was their ruler.

Then the Scottish people made Robert the Bruce their king. He was an earl and a relative of the late king. He banded the people together to fight the English, but Edward's army was too strong for them.

Twice the Scots were beaten and driven back. Their army was scattered and Robert the Bruce was forced to take flight.

He was hiding in a barn one day, feeling very hopeless when he noticed a spider. The spider was trying to throw a thread across to a beam to start a web. Every time she tried, the thread fell down. She tried six times, and failed. Then the seventh time, she succeeded.

When Robert the Bruce saw this, he knew he must not give up. He must keep trying, like the spider. So he gathered his troops together for another battle and, in 1314, he fought a great battle at Bannockburn. The English were put to flight and Scotland was free.

Fact or point of view?

Some of these statements are **facts**. Some are **points of view**.

♣ Read them and say which is which.

Robert the Bruce came from Scotland. Fact or point of view?

King Edward I was right to invade Scotland. Fact or point of view?

The English beat the Scots twice. Fact or point of view?

Robert was wrong to give up hope. Fact or point of view?

The spider was wiser than Robert. Fact or point of view?

Robert beat the English at Bannockburn. Fact or point of view?

This story happened a long time ago. Fact or point of view?

Robert the Bruce is Britain's greatest hero. Fact or point of view?

The Scots are better than the English. Fact or point of view?

The two giants

There once lived a giant called Finn MacCoul. He was a great hero and the strongest man in all Ireland. One day he heard that another giant, called Cuchullin, was looking for him. Cuchullin wanted a fight.

Now when Finn MacCoul heard this he was very frightened, so he ran straight home to ask his wife Oona what he should do.

'Make a cradle,' said Oona. 'Make it big enough to hold a grown man. While you're doing that, I'll bake some bread.' And so she did, but she hid a great lump of iron in every loaf. Then she dressed up Finn MacCoul like a baby and put him in the cradle.

Soon there was a stamping and there stood Cuchullin – a monster of a creature.

'Where's Finn MacCoul?' he roared.

'He's out looking for you,' said Oona, 'but while you're here, you can just turn the house around for me to give it a bit of an airing. Finn usually does it, but he was in such a temper he forgot.'

The giant picked the house up, turned it around and put it down again. Finn MacCoul, hiding in the cradle, shivered with fear. But Oona said nothing.

Presently she said, 'Finn always cracks the hill open to let the water out, but he was so mad to get at you that he forgot. Could you do it for me?'

The giant grunted and split the hillside with a single blow. Finn MacCoul's knees knocked inside the cradle, but Oona never said a word.

By and by she said, 'You must have some of my bread.'

Ireland

Cuchullin bit into a loaf and met an iron bar. It broke his tooth in two. He took another loaf. The same thing happened. He said, 'You bake hard bread mistress!'

'Why even the baby loves it,' said Oona.

Cuchullin looked at Finn MacCoul lying in his man-sized cradle. 'My,' he said, 'that's a big child.'

He put out a finger to tickle the baby's chin and Finn MacCoul snapped it clean off!

'Oh, he's nothing compared to his father,' said Oona.

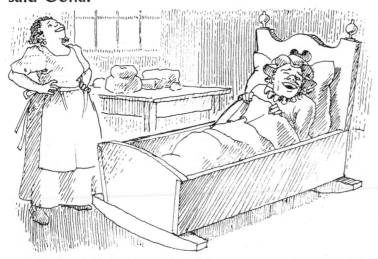

The giant let out a roar loud enough to wake the dead. Then he snatched up his big stick and ran.

'Wait,' called Oona. 'You haven't seen my husband.'

'And I don't want to!' Cuchullin cried. 'If that's the baby, I'm not fighting his father.'

With that he was gone. Oona and Finn MacCoul laughed until their sides ached, and they never had any trouble with Cuchullin again.

· Heroes' gallery ·

❖ Was Finn MacCoul real or imaginary?

❖ Draw some real heroes and heroines on the picture line.
Then draw some imaginary ones.

Real

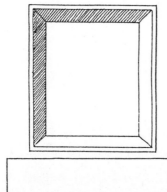  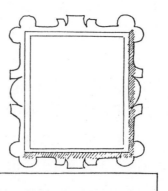 

Imaginary

  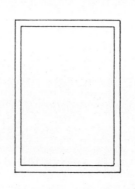 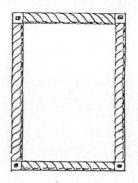

Name _____

Johnny Appleseed

Johnny Appleseed was born in the state of Massachusetts in America about 150 years ago.

Now in those days, there weren't many apple trees in America and Johnny Appleseed decided to put this right. He wanted everybody to enjoy the beautiful blossom in spring and the fruit in the autumn. So he spent his life planting apple trees all over America. He collected all the apple seeds he could find and put them into little bags. Then he went walking westward to the areas where no apple trees grew. When he found a good place he planted some seeds. The next year, he'd go back to see how the seedlings were doing.

Johnny Appleseed kept doing this for years. He planted apple orchards all over America, from the Rocky Mountains to Tennessee. He walked every step of the way, sleeping out in the open and eating whatever he could find.

He had all sorts of adventures.

One snowy night he was looking for shelter. He found a big hollow log to sleep in. So he built a fire, ate his supper and then began to crawl into the log. But when he got halfway in, he touched something furry. He was sharing the log with a bear. That night Johnny slept out in the snow!

It was hard, dangerous work, but he would never take any money for it. He did it because he wanted to help people, and to be remembered. And so he is. Most people have forgotten his real name, but American schoolchildren still remember Johnny Appleseed.

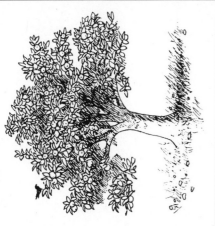

Improve your environment

Johnny Appleseed planted apple trees to make the world a better place.

♣ Draw a map of your own area.

♣ What could you plant to make it look good?

♣ How else could you improve it? Show all your improvements on your map.

N ↤

Key

The cave of the sleepers

A Welshman was crossing London Bridge one day, when he met a wizard. The wizard pointed to the hazel stick which the man was carrying and said, 'Show me the tree where you cut that stick, and I'll make you rich.'

'I cut it at Craig-y-Dinas[1] in Wales,' said the man.

'Then we will go there,' said the wizard, 'for I know by my magic powers that a great treasure is hidden under that tree.'

So the Welshman took the magician back to Craig-y-Dinas and showed him the hazel tree. They dug down to its roots and came upon a large flat stone. Together they heaved up the stone and found a flight of stairs leading to a dark cave. At the bottom of the stairs there hung a great bell.

The wizard slipped past it, being careful not to touch it. The Welshman did the same and together they tiptoed into a great cavern. All around, knights lay sleeping, calm and still in their shining armour. In the middle, on a raised bed, lay one greater than all the others with a crown of gold on his head and by his side were heaps of treasure.

'Hush,' said the wizard. 'Take all the treasure you want, but don't wake the sleepers. They are King Arthur and his knights, and they sleep until England needs them again.'

1. *Craig-y-Dinas* is pronounced CRAIG-I-DEENAS.

The Welshman and the wizard gathered up armfuls of the treasure, but as they made their way towards the stairs, the Welshman touched the bell. At once there was a long, low chime and the knights stirred in their sleep. A voice said, 'Is it time?'

'No,' said the wizard. 'Sleep on.' So the knights sighed and were still again.

Outside, in the daylight, the wizard and the Welshman shared out the gold and silver and went their separate ways.

As time passed, the Welshman spent all his share of the treasure and determined to go back to the cave again. Once more he lifted the stone slab and tiptoed down the shallow stairs. Once more he entered the cavern where the knights lay sleeping and gathered up all the gold and silver he could carry. However, in his greed, he gathered such a pile that he could not get past the bell. He knocked against it and set it ringing.

Just as before, the knights stirred and a voice said, 'Is it day?' The Welshman was too frightened to answer and, as he hesitated, the knights rose from their sleep.

One cried, 'A thief! a thief!' and with that they fell on him and beat him senseless.

When he came to, the man found himself all alone on a bare hillside. And although he searched and searched for the hazel tree and the entrance he never found them.

As for King Arthur and his knights, they probably sleep there still.

Arthur's country

There are many places which are named after King Arthur. Some of them are listed here.

♣ Look in an atlas to find each of the counties where these places occur. Mark each county's position with a cross on the map below.

Arthur's Cave (Gloucestershire, England)

Arthur's Chair (Cornwall, England)

Arthur's Chair (Northumberland, England)

Arthur's Seat (Lothian, Scotland)

Arthur's Seat (Cumbria, England)

Arthur's Well (Somerset, England)

Arthur's Palace (Somerset, England)

Arthur's Quoit (Anglesey, Wales)

Arthur's Chair (Powys, Wales)

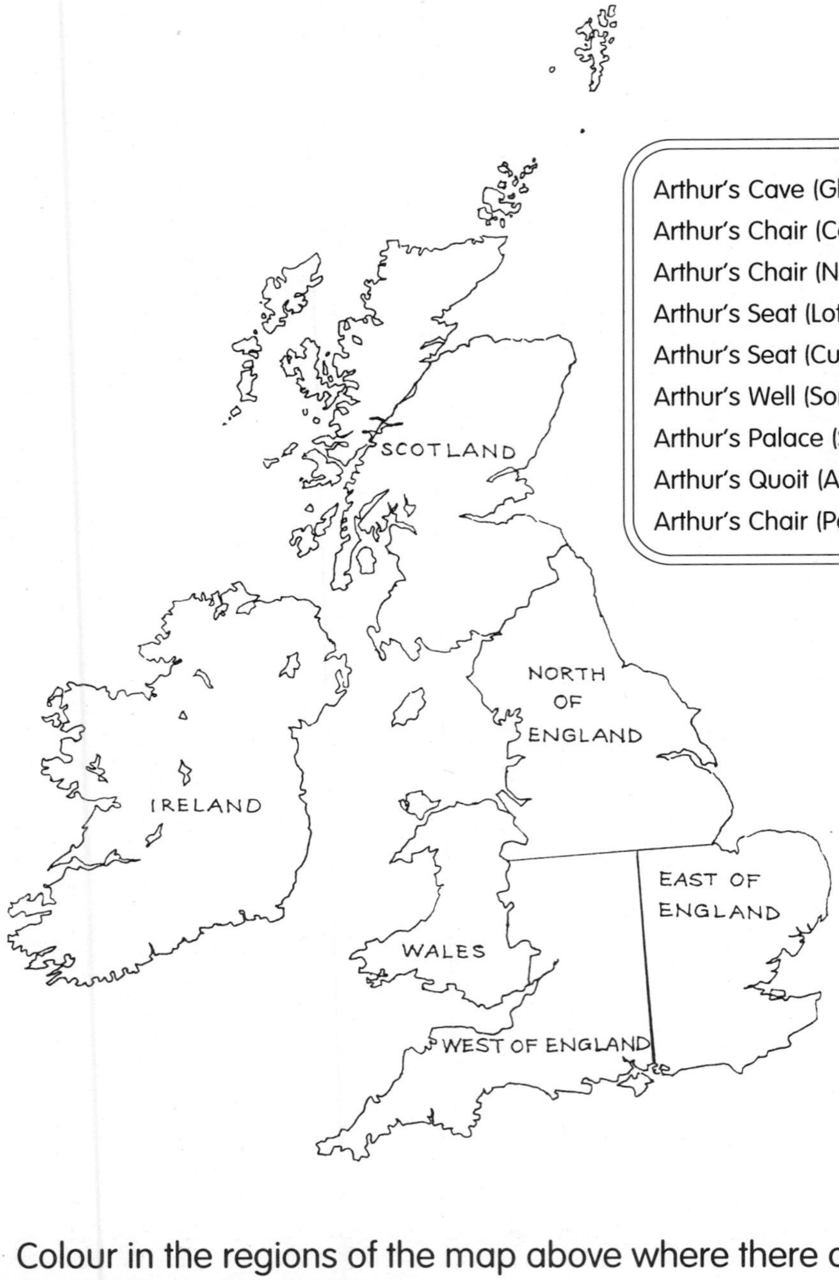

SCOTLAND

NORTH OF ENGLAND

EAST OF ENGLAND

WALES

WEST OF ENGLAND

IRELAND

♣ Colour in the regions of the map above where there are counties with places named after Arthur.

♣ Can you see any gaps? Why do you think this is so?

Robin Hood

Robin Hood lived in Sherwood Forest, near Nottingham. He was an outlaw who robbed the rich to give to the poor. The Sheriff of Nottingham was always trying to catch him and put him in his dungeon. However, Robin Hood was too clever to go near Nottingham. He stayed safe in the greenwood, hunting deer and feasting with his band of merry men.

Then, one day, the Sheriff thought of a trap. Robin Hood was a wonderful shot with a bow and arrow. He could shoot further and better than anyone else in the forest and the Sheriff knew this. So he sent out messengers north, south, east and west to announce a great archery match. It was to be held in Nottingham town and the prize was a golden arrow.

On the day of the archery match, the streets of Nottingham were thronged with lords and ladies, poor people and peasants who had come to watch the competition. All the best archers in England had gathered and, when everyone was ready, in rode the Sheriff of Nottingham on a milk-white horse. The herald blew his silver horn and the shooting began.

One by one the archers took their turn, until only ten were left. One of these, the Sheriff hoped, was Robin Hood. Some were too old and some were

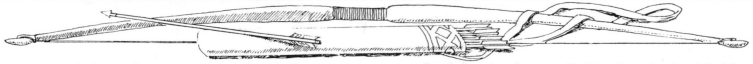

too young and the only man who it might have been was a tall beggar with a patch over one eye, but he was dressed in scarlet, while Robin always wore Lincoln green.

'Why then,' said the Sheriff, 'Robin Hood is afraid to come. So he's a coward, as well as a law-breaker and a thief.'

The final ten archers shot again, two arrows each, and the Sheriff chose the best of them. Now only three archers were left. One was Gilbert of the Red Cap, one was Adam of the Dell and the last was the beggar in scarlet.

Gilbert shot first and it was a good shot. Adam went next and his was even better. Last of all came the ragged man. His aim was so true that his arrow split Adam's clean in two and went to the heart of the target. The crowd cheered, the lords and ladies nodded and the Sheriff of Nottingham gave the beggar in scarlet the golden arrow.

Back in the forest, Robin laughed with his men as he took off the ragged scarlet clothes and the eye-patch. They hung the golden arrow in a greenwood tree and all that night they feasted and sang and talked of their great adventure. That same night another arrow flew through the window of the Sheriff's great hall in Nottingham. Tied around it was a piece of paper which said:

Now heaven bless your Grace this day,
Say all men of Sherwood.
For you did give the prize away
To merry Robin Hood.

In olden days...

There are many stories about Robin Hood, but nobody knows whether he was a real person. We **do** know that the stories are very old.

♣ Look for clues in the story of Robin Hood and in the pictures which tell you that the story comes from a long time ago.

Clue 1:

Clue 2:

Clue 3:

Clue 4:

Clue 5:

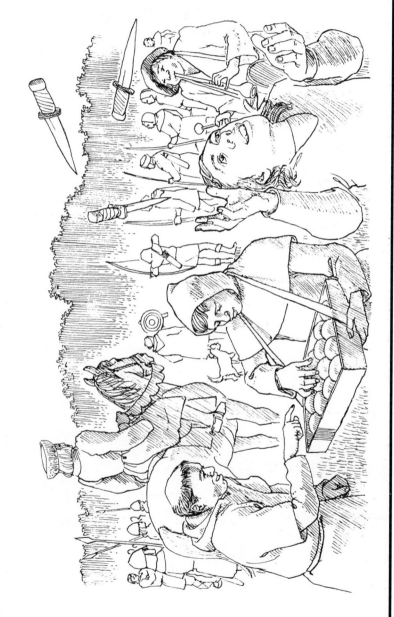

Robin Hood

Name _____

Wanted!

♣ Finish off this poster for the Sheriff. Include a description of Robin Hood and his alleged crimes.

Wanted
dead or alive

Robin Hood

Dick Whittington

Along time ago, there lived in England a poor boy called Dick Whittington. Now Dick had heard that the streets of London were paved with gold, so one day he tied up all his belongings in a handkerchief and off he went to seek his fortune.

When he got to London, he found that the pavements were made of hard stone and he could find neither work nor food. So he wandered the streets getting hungrier and hungrier until at last he came to the door of a rich merchant called Mr Fitzwarren. Mr Fitzwarren gave him a good meal and a job in his kitchen.

Dick worked for the cook, and slept in a bed in the attic. But there were rats up there and they kept him awake. So when he'd earned a penny, he bought himself a little cat to catch the rats.

One day, Mr Fitzwarren called all the servants together. He told them he'd bought a ship and was setting sail for foreign parts. He was taking things to sell and he told the servants he would sell things for them too. Everyone had something to send, except for Dick. All he owned was the little black cat. So he sent it off on the ship.

When the master had gone, things got harder for Dick. Mr Fitzwarren's daughter, Alice, was very kind to him, but the cook was cruel. She hit him with a wooden spoon, gave him all the hard work to do and kept him so short of food that he decided to run away. He packed his things and walked out of the house. He didn't get very far, though.

England

He was sitting on a milestone, wondering which way to go, when he heard Bow Bells ring out:

Turn again Whittington
Thou worthy citizen
Lord Mayor of London.

'Lord Mayor of London!' said Dick, and he turned and went back to the Fitzwarrens' house.

It was lucky he did, for when the ship returned, it brought great news. The ship had sailed down the coast of north Africa until it came to a kingdom which was plagued with mice. They ate up the corn and nibbled the green shoots and nested in the king's own throne.

Mr Fitzwarren saw what was happening and knew the answer at once. He sent for Dick's cat and set it to work.

Within a day, there wasn't a mouse to be seen in all the kingdom. When the king saw this, he offered Mr Fitzwarren a fortune in gold to buy the cat. He paid more for it than all the rest of the cargo put together. Mr Fitzwarren brought this money back to give to Dick.

So Dick Whittington became a rich man and he married his master's daughter, Alice. He did indeed become Lord Mayor of London, just as Bow Bells had foretold and he and his wife lived happily for the rest of their lives.

The real Dick Whittington

Dick Whittington was a real person. This is what we know about him.

He was born in Gloucestershire.

He married Alice Fitzwarren.

He was Lord Mayor of London three times.

He was kind to the poor and built houses for them.

He lived about 600 years ago.

Over time people have forgotten the real facts and have turned his life into a story.

Some nursery rhymes are based on real people and real happenings.

♣ See if you can guess these:

King Cole ruled Britain in the third century. He built Colchester. His daughter played the fiddle.

_____

Between 1664 and 1665, England suffered from a great plague. The first sign of the illness was a ring of red spots, followed by sneezing. To try to prevent it, people carried posies of herbs.

_____

About 1,000 years ago, the Norsemen attacked London and pulled down London Bridge.

_____

Frederick, Duke of York, was son of King George III. He commanded the king's army.

_____

Name _____

Special people timeline

Dick Whittington was a real person. He lived about 600 years ago.

✤ Draw him on the timeline.

✤ Now draw the other events on the timeline.

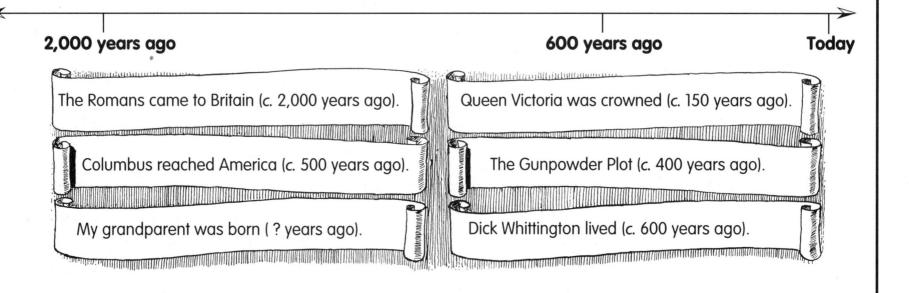

2,000 years ago   **600 years ago**   **Today**

The Romans came to Britain (*c.* 2,000 years ago).

Queen Victoria was crowned (*c.* 150 years ago).

Columbus reached America (*c.* 500 years ago).

The Gunpowder Plot (*c.* 400 years ago).

My grandparent was born (? years ago).

Dick Whittington lived (*c.* 600 years ago).

✤ Draw three more special historical events on the timeline.

Drake's cannon-ball

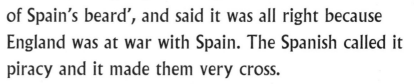

Sir Francis Drake was a real person who lived in the time of Queen Elizabeth I. He was a great sailor and he had many adventures. When he was a pirate, he stole the king of Spain's treasure. As an explorer, he was the first Englishman to sail round the world. Lastly, he was a great admiral who defeated the Spanish Armada.

All these things really happened, but because he was so special many other stories grew up around him. In these stories he was a kind of wizard with magical powers. Here is one of them.

Drake wanted to marry a Somerset girl called Elizabeth Sydenham, but her family turned him down because he was poor. So Drake went off to seek his fortune, raiding the Spanish treasure ships as they came sailing back from America, loaded with gold and silver stolen from the Incas and the Aztecs. He called this 'singeing the King of Spain's beard', and said it was all right because England was at war with Spain. The Spanish called it piracy and it made them very cross.

All this took time. Back in England, Elizabeth Sydenham's family had found a rich husband for her to marry and the date was set for the wedding. Everything was ready and the bride was walking down the aisle when suddenly, far away in the Atlantic, Drake had a vision of what was happening.

He put his telescope to his eye and looked for a thousand miles or more, across the world to Stogumber Church, where the wedding was taking place. When he saw the bride and bridegroom, he let out such a bellow of rage that the whole ship

Tudors

trembled. He called to his gunners to load the great cannon and they crammed in all the gunpowder they had and fired a single shot. The cannon-ball travelled by way of the sea and the land, until it finished up, white-hot and smoking, at the feet of the wedding guests.

Everyone was terrified. The wedding was called off and Elizabeth Sydenham was left in peace until Drake came back, rich and famous, to marry her. And in Coombe Sydenham House, which is where Elizabeth Sydenham used to live, you can still see a big round stone. It's blackened and burned and about the size of a football. Some people say it's a meteorite which fell from the sky, but others say it's Drake's cannon-ball which he fired across the world.

Name _____

Famous Elizabethans

These three famous people all lived in the time of Queen Elizabeth I.

✤ Use books to find out as much as you can about them. Choose the most important bits to write in the captions.

Sir Francis Drake   **Sir Walter Raleigh**   **William Shakespeare**

Name _____

Drake's cannon-ball

The legendary Drake

Some of these statements about Sir Francis Drake
are true. Some are legends.

♣ Use books to find out which is which and write
'true' or 'legend' in each box.

He lived at the time of Queen Elizabeth I.

He lies sleeping in his hammock and will
return in Britain's hour of need.

He sailed round the world in a ship called
the *Golden Hind*.

He used magic to call up a wind.

He was playing bowls when the Spanish
Armada came.

He used fire-ships to break up the
Spanish Armada.

He singed the King of Spain's beard.

♣ Why do you think there are so many
stories about Drake? Read the books to
find out more about his life.

My hero!

♣ What is a hero or heroine? Find out what these words mean.

♣ Draw your favourite hero or heroine here and write why you have chosen him or her.

I have chosen my hero/heroine because _____

_____

_____

_____

General sheet

Peoples from the past

❖ Match these peoples from the past with something special that they did.

❖ Then arrange them in order and make a timeline.

❖ Use reference books to help you to find out something each of them did.

1. *c.* means *circa* or about. **2**. **BC** means Before Christ. **3**. **AD** means *Anno Domini* or After Christ.

Some peoples from the past	**An important event**
Egyptians *c.*[1] 3000 **BC**[2] – 30 **BC**	King Alfred drives back the Vikings (**AD** 878).
Anglo-Saxons *c.* **AD**[3] 410 – **AD** 1000	The Aztecs finish their capital city, Tenochtitlan (**AD** 1340).
Romans *c.* 750 **BC** – **AD** 410	Leif Ericsson reaches America (**AD** 1000).
Greeks *c.* 850 **BC** – 30 **BC**	Occupation of Britain (**AD** 43 – **AD** 450).
Vikings *c.* **AD** 780 – **AD** 1150	The Greeks win the Battle of Salamis (480 **BC**).
Aztecs *c.* **AD** 1325 – **AD** 1521	Tutankhamen is buried (1323 **BC**).

Thor goes fishing

This is a story about one of the Viking gods.

Thor was the god of war and thunder. He was a brave fighter. It was Thor who made war on the frost giants, who lived in the cold lands of the  north. The frost giants were the enemies of the gods and they hated Thor most of all because he had killed so many of them.

Thor was giving a feast for the gods and he needed a brewing kettle big enough to brew beer for all of them. He searched high and low, but no one could help him. Then, he heard that a frost giant called Hymir owned such a kettle. So he set out and rode until he came to Hymir's palace standing alone on the edge of the cold North Sea. Hymir's wife was at the door and when she saw

Thor she looked afraid. 'If my husband finds you here, he'll kill you,' she said. 'You must hide and I'll break the news to him gently.'

As night fell, in came Hymir, shaking icicles from his beard. When his wife told him that Thor the giant-killer was there, he became very angry. His wife pleaded and at last he said, 'He's a guest in my house, so I suppose I must let him be. Tomorrow we will go fishing together.'

Early next morning they set off. They rowed out into the deep ocean and began to catch whales. Presently, Thor felt a tug on his line which nearly pulled him into the water.

Vikings

He held on as best he could and saw, far below him, the shape of a great green head rising out of the water. There were spikes and scales and a long snake-like neck. He had caught the World Serpent that coils around the Earth.

Still Thor held on. Higher and higher rose the World Serpent hissing with fury until Hymir, with a cry of fear, cut the line and the World Serpent sank back into the deep again.

That night the giant's wife roasted the whales and they ate them all. Then Hymir grew sleepy and when he nodded off, Thor took the brewing kettle and slipped away with it.

He hadn't gone very far before he saw Hymir coming after him with all the men he could muster. He was waving a sword.

Thor threw his magic hammer at Hymir and it hit him on the head and knocked him out. Like magic, it returned to his hand and he threw it again and again until he had got rid of all of his pursuers. Then he carried the brewing kettle back to the gods' great hall at Asgard and many a gallon of beer was brewed in it for the gods' feasts.

As for the World Serpent, it sank back to the bottom of the sea and there it will stay until the day of *Ragnarok*[1] and the last battle of the gods.

1. *'Ragnarok'* is a Viking word meaning 'the end of the world'. When, they believed, all the enemies of the gods would gather for a last battle in which many would die.

Name _____

Viking gods and goddesses

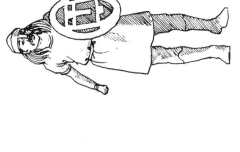

Thor was the god of war and of thunder.

Here are some of the other gods and goddesses he invited to his feast.

Loki was the god of fire. He was a trickster.

Tyr, or Tew, was a great hero. He gave his hand to save the other gods.

Odin, or Woden, was the chief of the gods. He had only one eye. He was very wise.

Freya was the most beautiful of the goddesses. She wore a magic necklace and a cloak made of feathers.

♣ Four of the Viking gods and goddesses gave their names to days of the week. Can you find out which they are?

Day	Name of god/goddess
Monday	
Tuesday	
Wednesday	
Thursday	
Friday	
Saturday	
Sunday	

♣ Can you find out where the other days of the week got their names from?

Thor goes fishing

World Serpent puzzle

✤ Find out these facts about the Viking gods and write them in the snake.

- What was Thor's special weapon?
- What was his special weather?
- What day of the week did Thor give his name to?
- Find out the names of two more Viking gods.
- Where did the gods live?

✤ Find out what a Viking boat looked like and draw a picture of Thor fishing for the World Serpent. You could use the back of this sheet.

Plumed Serpent

Plumed Serpent was an Aztec[1] god. The Aztec people believed he ruled the sky and the sun, the winds and the morning star.

They believed that for many years he had lived on Earth and that during that time he taught the Aztecs how to grow maize, how to weave and to work gold and silver. The years of his rule were happy ones, and the Aztecs grew rich.

However, as he grew old, other gods plotted against him. There was one in particular, called Smoking Mirror, who wanted to harm him. One day he thought of a way. He came to Plumed Serpent and said, 'Look, and I will show you something wonderful.'

Plumed Serpent turned to look. In his hand the other god held a mirror and in it Plumed Serpent saw his own reflection. It was that of a tired old man with a wrinkled face and sad eyes. He had never come across a mirror before and he said, 'Who is that poor old man?'

'It's you,' said Smoking Mirror. Plumed Serpent was horrified. He was afraid that if his people saw him, they would think he was too old to rule and would fight against him. He ran away from the mirror to hide himself in a deep, dark cave.

Smoking Mirror followed him and made him look in the mirror again. Then he gave Plumed Serpent a wonderful cloak made from feathers and a snake mask made from the finest turquoise to cover his wrinkled face. It was these which gave Plumed Serpent his name and from then on he wore them always.

1. The Aztec people lived in what is now Mexico before the Spanish conquest during the sixteenth century.

Name _____

The Aztec civilization

For many years after this, Plumed Serpent remained on Earth, but at last a time came when enemies were attacking his kingdom and the crops had failed. Plumed Serpent knew then that he was bringing bad luck on his people and that he must leave them.

He set off over the mountains accompanied by many servants. As he walked, he cast away his rich clothes and his jewels and one by one his servants left him until he was all alone. He came at last to the sea and there, by magic, he made a raft of snakes. He rode away into the east and was never seen again.

However, the Aztecs believed that one day he would come back. They said he would come sailing out of the east in a strange, shining ship. He would be surrounded by thunder and lightning and they would know him by his pale skin and his golden hair. For many years the Aztecs waited and watched for his coming, but he never returned.

Picture writing

The Aztecs used picture writing to tell their stories. This is how they showed Plumed Serpent.

♣ Tell his story in pictures.

The Benin civilization

The oba of Benin

When the Portuguese explorers first came to West Africa, they found a great kingdom called Benin. The oba, or king, of Benin was named Esigie and there are many stories about him. Here is one of them.

When Esigie was a young man, he was not very wise and he made many enemies. One of them was his chief adviser. Esigie had made a fool of him and the man was so angry that he became determined to harm Esigie. He went to the king of the neighbouring country and persuaded him to invade Benin.

Esigie, hearing the news, told his chiefs to gather their men and get ready for war. However, he was not a popular ruler and the men refused to fight.

'Kill the ones who refuse,' said the king.

'Then we must kill the whole army,' said the chiefs. 'Nobody will fight for you.'

Esigie tried everything to make his people fight, but nothing worked. The enemy troops were getting closer and closer to the capital city, killing and burning as they came, and still the Benin soldiers refused to take up arms.

At last, when the enemy was just around the corner, an old priest spoke up. He walked through the streets of the capital banging a gong and calling to the young men to fight.

'This is your city,' he said. 'When the enemy take it, they won't just kill the king. They'll kill you and your families. If you won't fight for the king, fight for yourselves.'

When the soldiers heard this, they knew he was right and they got ready to go to war.

After a great battle they defeated the enemy and were driving them back when a bird flew across the sky crying out to them. It was an ibis and in Benin the cry of the ibis is very unlucky indeed.

The Benin soldiers stared at it. Nobody dared to move for fear of bad luck. When King Esigie saw what had happened, he rode forward on his great horse.

'Go or stay as you please,' he said, 'but I am not afraid of a bird's cry, and I ride on to attack the enemy.' With that he charged straight towards the enemy army.

His men followed, for they saw that, despite his faults, the young king was a good leader and a brave man. They put the enemy to flight and Esigie went back to his palace a wiser and humbler man.

The first thing he did on his return home was to pass a new law. It stated that all chiefs must carry a staff tipped with the head of an ibis to remind the people of Benin of the great battle against their enemy; and the chiefs of Benin carry such staffs to this day.

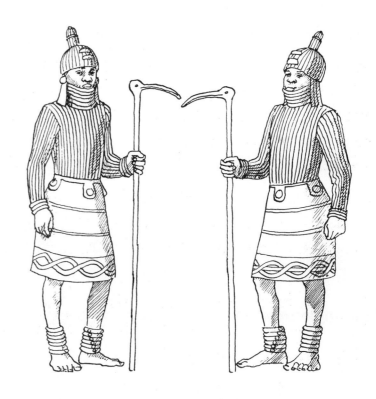

The oba of Benin

Days to remember

Like the people of Benin, we remember important things that have happened in our history; some happy, others sad.

❖ What do we remember on these days?

Bonfire Night _____

_____

_____

Poppy Day _____

_____

_____

Oak Apple Day _____

_____

_____

Burns' Night _____

_____

_____

D-Day _____

_____

_____

Beowulf

There was once a king called Hrothgar who built a great hall. There he sat every evening, feasting and drinking with his men. When the feast was over, the men lay down by the fire and slept until morning.

One night, when the world was still, a water troll came out of the lake and killed every one of them. Hrothgar set soldiers to guard the hall, but in the morning they were found dead too. The same thing happened night after night until people began to say that the hall was cursed and nobody dared to stay there after the sun had set.

Now a man called Beowulf came to the hall. He was a great hero and as strong as ten men. When he heard of the curse, he asked if he might sleep in the hall with his men, and King Hrothgar agreed. That night there was a great feast in the hall. When darkness fell, all the king's men withdrew, leaving only Beowulf and his men.

In the dark of the night, when even the stars were sleeping, they heard soft footsteps padding around the hall and there was a smell of river weed and marsh gas.

Beowulf and his men drew their swords. The door burst open and in came Grendel, the water troll, ten feet tall and with skin like a crocodile's. Grendel seized the first one of Beowulf's men and tore him clean in two.

Saxons

Then all the others fell on him, but his skin was so thick that no sword could pierce it. So Beowulf wrestled with him, hurling himself back and forth until Grendel, trying to escape, tore himself away and left his arm in Beowulf's grasp. He managed to get back to the lake, leaving a great trail of blood behind him, but there he died.

Now Grendel had a mother who was even stronger and more cruel than her son and when she saw her son return dying, she made up her mind to take revenge. So she in turn came out of the lake to prowl around the hall. She found many people sleeping there, for they thought it was now safe, but she attacked and killed every one of them.

When Beowulf heard of this, he tracked her to her lair, following the trail of blood which Grendel had left. Diving deep, he met her in an underwater cave in the roots of a mountain. It was littered with broken weapons and with the bones of dead heroes,

captured and killed by Grendel and his mother. There Beowulf wrestled with her and killed her at last with an enchanted sword.

King Hrothgar offered Beowulf gold and jewels and half of his kingdom, but he would take no reward. He sailed back to his own country where he became a great king and a dragon-slayer... but that's another story.

In the great hall

The picture below shows the outside and inside of a great hall in Saxon times.

✤ Use reference books to help you to draw the people who are feasting in the great hall. Include details of their clothes and weapons.

✤ Find out what food they ate in Beowulf's time and draw it on the tables.

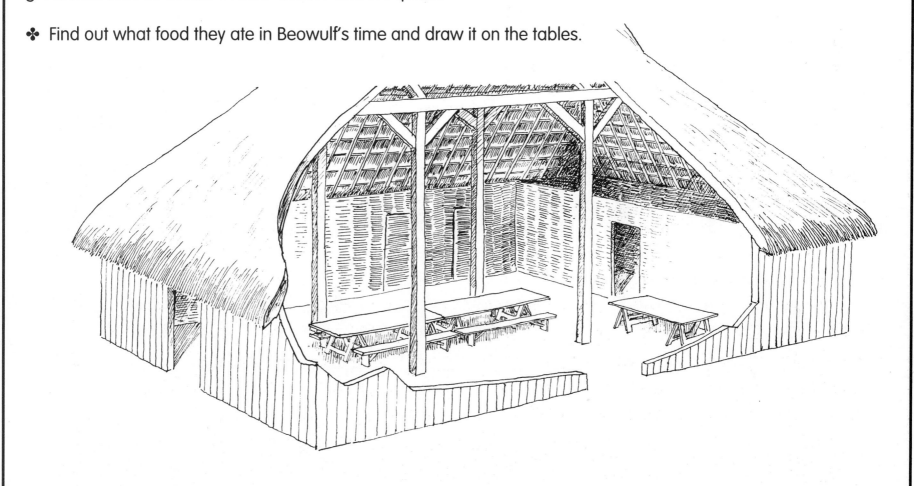

Beowulf

Name _____

Riddles and sagas

Beowulf is a story from Saxon times. In the evening, when the day's work was done, such stories were told in the great hall at the heart of each Saxon settlement.

As well as stories, the Saxons enjoyed songs and riddles.

♣ Here is one of their riddles. Can you solve it?

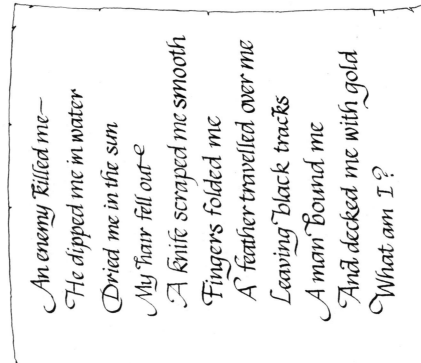

An enemy killed me—
He dipped me in water
Dried me in the sun
My hair fell out
A knife scraped me smooth
Fingers folded me
A feather travelled over me
Leaving black tracks
A man bound me
And decked me with gold
What am I ?

♣ Make up your own riddle about someone or something in the Beowulf story. See if your friend can solve it.

Romulus and Remus

The city of Rome stands beside the River Tiber. It is built on seven hills and it was once the centre of a great empire. The Romans believed that the city was founded 700 years before the birth of Christ by two brothers called Romulus and Remus. The Romans said it happened like this.

There was once a priestess called Rhea Silvia, who served the goddess Vesta. Rhea Silvia was very beautiful and the god Mars, seeing her one day, fell in love with her. In time, she bore him twin sons called Romulus and Remus.

When Rhea Silvia's father got to hear about the birth, he was very angry with her. Anyone who became a servant of Vesta had to swear a solemn promise that they would never marry or have children. Rhea Silvia had broken this promise and shamed her family. So her father decided to try and keep it a secret and he told his servants to take the boys and drown them in the River Tiber.

When the men reached the river, they could not harden their hearts enough to kill the babies, so they left them on the riverside. There a mother wolf found them and fed them with her milk. The babies stayed with the wolf until a shepherd called Faustulus came upon them and he brought them up as his own children.

When they grew up, the boys decided to build a city on the spot where they had been found.

'We'll name it after me,' said Remus.

'No, we'll name it after me,' said Romulus.

The brothers quarrelled so bitterly that a fight broke out and in that fight Romulus killed his brother, Remus. So he alone built the new city and it was called Rome after him.

For ever afterwards the Romans dated their letters and papers from the year in which Romulus founded Rome – because that was the very start of their great empire.

Name _____

Romulus and Remus

Where to build Rome?

♣ Imagine that you are Romulus and that you have to choose a place to build your city. It must be near water, near good land for farming and safe from enemies.

♣ List the good and bad points for each of the suggested sites, A to F.

A _____

B _____

C _____

D _____

E _____

F _____

I think that site _____ is best because _____

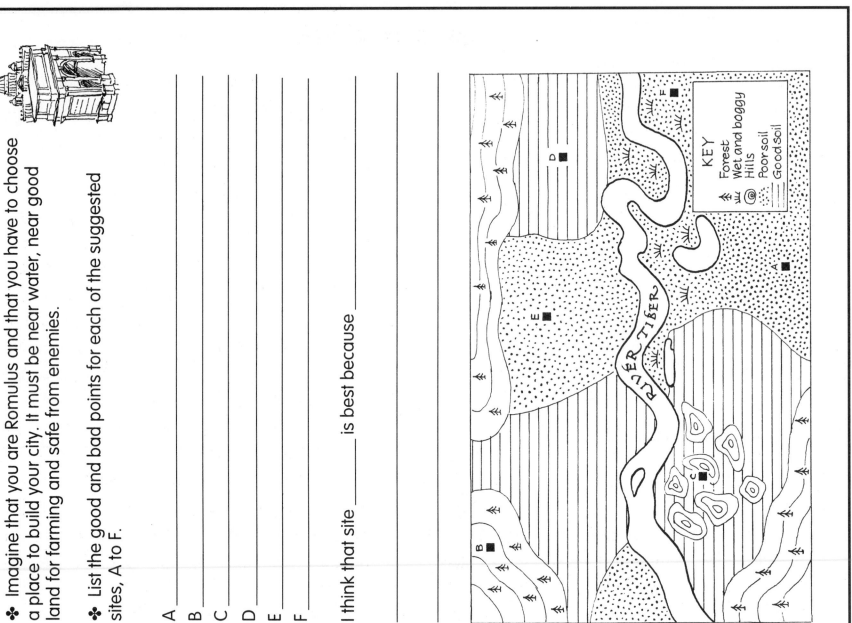

KEY
Forest
Wet and boggy
Hills
Poor soil
Good soil

RIVER TIBER

Pandora's box

This is a story that the Ancient Greeks told to explain how evil came into the world.

Long ago, there were no people on Earth. There were only the gods and the Titans. The Titans were giants who lived for ever. Zeus, the king of the gods, made people out of clay and breathed life into them. But they were cold and hungry because he kept the secret of fire from them.

There was a Titan called Prometheus, who felt sorry for the mortals and he stole fire from heaven to give to them.

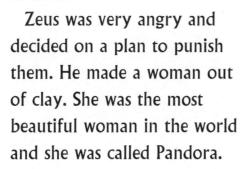

Zeus was very angry and decided on a plan to punish them. He made a woman out of clay. She was the most beautiful woman in the world and she was called Pandora.

Each of the gods gave her a special gift and then Zeus breathed life into her and led her to the house of Epimetheus, the brother of the Titan Prometheus, who was the leader of the mortals. When Epimetheus saw her he fell in love with her and married her and they lived together very happily.

However, in the house of Epimetheus there was a box. It was a special, magic box and Epimetheus warned Pandora that it held all sorts of secrets and that she must never, never open it. Pandora listened and promised to do as he said.

But as time went by, she longed to know what secrets lay in the box. She wondered about it night and day until she could neither sleep nor eat.

One day, when her husband was away, Pandora could bear it no longer. She stretched out her hand to the box and raised the lid. As she did so, there

came a blast of darkness and a bitter cold wind. Out from the box flew all the sorrows of the world – sickness and old age, war and pain, and every other misery that troubles the human race.

As they swept past her, Pandora slammed the lid down, but it was too late. The evils were loose in the world and there was nothing she could do to get them back. But in the box she heard a fluttering sound as if one last creature was struggling to get out. It was Hope. Hope had been put in the box to give people strength to go on, and now Pandora let it go free too.

So that is how Zeus got his revenge on the mortals, for he let loose on them all the sorrows of the world. But at least they had Hope to comfort them.

Up on Mount Olympus

Here are some of the gods and goddesses of Ancient Greece.

❖ Use reference books to find out more about them.

Zeus   Athene   Aphrodite   Apollo   Poseidon

❖ Can you guess what gift each god or goddess might have given to Pandora?

Osiris

Long ago, in the land of Egypt, there lived a god called Osiris, who was good and golden and kind. However, Osiris had a brother called Set who was as wicked as Osiris was good. Set hated his brother and plotted to kill him, but Isis, the wife of Osiris, kept her husband safe.

Now it happened that Isis went away on a long journey, leaving Osiris alone. Set saw his chance. He invited Osiris and many others to a great feast and when everyone had eaten and drunk their fill, his servants brought in a beautiful wooden chest decorated with gold and painted with magic signs.

Set said, 'I will give this chest to the man who fits it exactly.' So one by one all the guests tried it. Some were too tall and some were too short and nobody was the exact size of the chest. At last Osiris took his turn. The chest fitted him perfectly, touching his head and his heel.

Then Set cried out in triumph. He slammed down the lid and sealed the chest with molten lead. It was thrown into the River Nile and floated far away into the land of Biblos, where it lodged against a tree. In time the roots of the tree grew up around it until it was quite hidden and no sign remained of the god Osiris.

When Isis returned nobody dared tell her what had become of her husband for they were afraid of Set. So she searched far and wide until at last she came to the land of Biblos where she met an old man who said, 'I have not seen your husband, lady, but by the River Nile there is a tree and every night a great star shines over it as if there is something wonderful hidden there.'

When Isis saw the tree, she knew she had found her husband. But Set got to hear of it and he feared that, by her magic, Isis might bring Osiris back to life. So he took the body of Osiris and cut it into many pieces. Then he scattered them up and down the Nile, all over Egypt.

But Isis would not give up. Again she searched until she had found every piece of her dead husband.

When all the pieces were gathered together, she brought his body back to life again in one great night of magic. But for all her magic she could only keep him alive for one night, so after that she washed his body and wrapped it with bandages and sent it to the Land of the Dead.

So Osiris became the god of the dead and the Ancient Egyptians believed that when they died, they would go to join him in the Afterworld. They thought that Isis would bring their bodies back to life, as she had done her husband's, and that they would live in the land of the dead for as long as their bodies lasted. This is why bodies were mummified, to make them last for ever.

Name _____

Make your own mummy

You will need:

- modelling clay;
- bandages;
- beads and sequins;
- tissue paper;
- adhesive;
- a shoebox;
- pencils and pens;
- scissors.

1 Make a figure out of modelling clay.

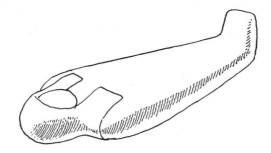

2 Wrap it in bandages. Wrap beads and sequins in the bandages. These are lucky charms.

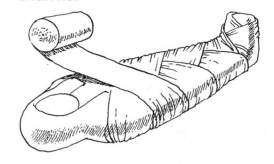

3 Soak strips of tissue paper in adhesive. Smooth them over the bandages to make a mummy case.

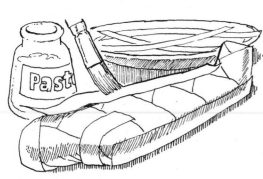

4 Paint the mummy case with hieroglyphs. Draw on the 'Eye of Horus'.

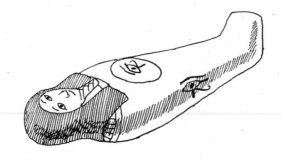

5 Decorate a shoebox in the same way, to make a coffin. Put the mummy case in the coffin.

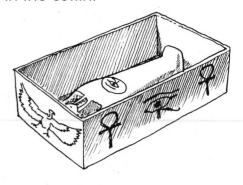

The 40 judges

Some of the 40 judges

The Ancient Egyptians believed that people faced many tests on their way through the Underworld. Forty judges questioned them about their lives. Then Thoth, the scribe of the gods, tested them to see if they spoke the truth. Anubis, the guardian of the tomb, weighed their hearts. If they had been good, Horus, the sky god, led them to Osiris. However, if they lied to Thoth then their hearts were eaten and the bad might suffer a variety of fates, depending on their wickedness.

✤ Draw a dead person's journey through the Underworld to Osiris.

Anubis   **Thoth**   **Horus**   **Osiris**

Name _____

Theseus and the Minotaur

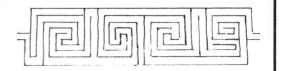

On the island of Crete, there's a ruined palace. It is called Knossos and the people of Crete tell this story about it.

Long ago a king called Minos lived at Knossos. He was a strong king and everyone was afraid of him. But King Minos had a dreadful secret. His son was a monster who was half man and half bull. He was called the Minotaur and he ate human flesh.

King Minos kept his son hidden away in a maze underneath the palace, but the Minotaur had to be fed. Minos so frightened the king of Athens that he agreed to send Minos seven young men and women every year. They were locked up in the maze to be killed and eaten by the Minotaur. Even if they managed to escape, they never came out because the maze was so complicated that no one had ever managed to find a way back to the entrance. This went on year after year until Theseus, the prince of Athens, made up his mind to stop it. He offered to go to Crete himself, hoping that he might succeed in killing the Minotaur.

Theseus was very handsome and when King Minos' daughter, Ariadne, saw him, she made up her mind that she would save him from the Minotaur. So she waited until everyone was asleep and then she slipped into the room where he lay and whispered, 'Theseus, listen to me. Tomorrow you must face the Minotaur and nobody has ever done that and lived to tell the tale, but I can keep

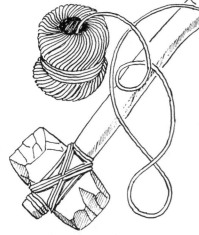

you safe if you do as I say. First, take this ball of string. When you enter the maze, you must tie it to the doorpost and unwind it as you go. Second, take this stone axe. It is magic and it will kill the Minotaur. Remember my advice and all will be well.'

So in the morning, when the guards came to fetch him, Theseus took with him the ball of string and the axe. As soon as he entered the maze, he tied the string to the doorpost and began to make his way to the heart of the maze. There were so many twists and turns that he soon lost his way, but all the time he could hear the roaring of the Minotaur and follow the trail of bones which led to its lair.

Then suddenly it charged out of the darkness and Theseus stepped back, swinging the axe. He cut off its head with a single blow for, as the princess had promised, the axe was a magic one. He turned to find his way out, but he was quite lost. Then he remembered the ball of string and he followed it to thread his way back to the entrance to the maze and out into the air again, where he found the princess waiting for him.

Ariadne ran away with Theseus and together they set sail for Athens. However, the princess never got there. They stopped at an island and, while she was asleep, Theseus forgot all about her and sailed on alone. He went on to become a great king and there are many stories about him, but what became of the princess, nobody knows.

Left behind!

♣ What is Ariadne thinking? Imagine you are Ariadne and tell the story from her point of view.

♣ What is Theseus thinking?

♣ Why do you think he left Ariadne on the island?

Was there really a King Minos?

People called 'archaeologists' dig at special sites to find things which tell them about the past. Some archaeologists believed that there really was a King Minos. They dug up the ruined palace at Knossos and this is what they found.

A bull's head mask.

A double axe sign.

Paintings of people and bulls.

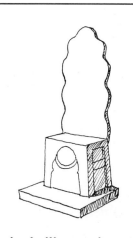

A chair like a throne.

A statue of a young girl.

♣ Imagine that you are an archaeologist who went to Knossos.

♣ Write a report about the evidence that you found.
- What does it mean?
- Do you think King Minos really existed?
- How does the story fit with the evidence that you have found?

Jason and the Argonauts

This is a very old story which comes from Ancient Greece.

Long, long ago there lived a young prince called Jason. When Jason was a baby, his wicked uncle, Pelias, killed Jason's father and stole his kingdom.

When Jason was older, Pelias decided to get rid of him too, so he dared him to go in search of the Golden Fleece.

Now Jason knew that nobody had ever come back alive from such a quest. The Golden Fleece hung on a tree at the world's end in the land of Colchis. It was guarded by a deadly serpent, whose very breath was poisonous.

But Jason was too proud to refuse.

He sent for Argus, the greatest shipbuilder in all of Greece, and ordered him to make a ship with fifty oars. Jason named it *Argo*, and when it was finished, he sent messengers to all four corners of the land, calling for heroes to come with him on his journey.

The *Argo* set sail in the summer when the storms were over and travelled until they came to the clashing rocks at the gateway to the Black Sea. These were floating masses of rock which crashed together and crushed any ship which came through. But Jason let loose a bird and as it flew between the rocks, they clashed together, just missing its tail, leaving a clear way so the *Argo* could follow after.

The Argonauts sailed into the Black Sea and came, after many adventures, to the land of Colchis to look for the Golden Fleece. But the king of Colchis, who did not want to let the fleece go, said Jason could only have it if he could first plough and sow a field with dragon's teeth.

Now the king's daughter, Medea, had fallen in love with Jason and helped him to plough the field. In the morning he planted the dragon's teeth, but within minutes they had grown into men, armed men, who turned on Jason and attacked him. However, Jason had been warned by Medea and he knew what to do. He threw a stone into the middle of them. At once they began fighting among themselves until every last one of them was dead.

The king was very angry, but he pretended to keep his promise. However, Jason did not trust him. So, during the night, he and Medea crept out of the palace and went to the magic garden where the Golden Fleece hung on an apple tree. Then, while Medea sang the serpent to sleep, Jason took down the fleece from the tree and carried it away.

Jason and his heroes and the Princess Medea all sailed away from Colchis as fast as they could, with the king in hot pursuit. They gave him the slip and brought the Golden Fleece, in triumph, back to Iolcos where it became the greatest treasure of the kingdom. And the story of Jason and his Argonauts has been remembered ever since.

Jason and the Argonauts

Evidence of the past

No ship has survived from Ancient Greek times as they all rotted away long ago. We can't be certain what they looked like, but we have pictures from Ancient Greek times to help us.

✤ Look at the picture on this Ancient Greek vase. Can you match the labels with the correct part of the ship? The first one has been done for you.

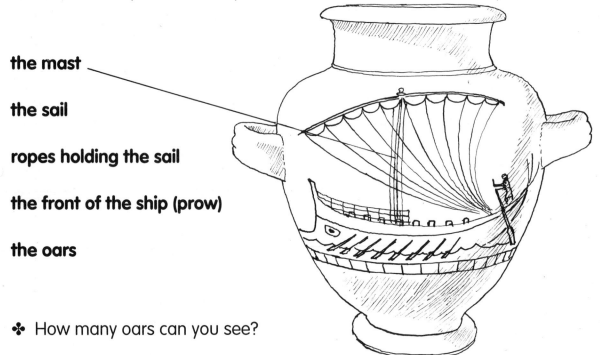

the mast

the sail

ropes holding the sail

the front of the ship (prow)

the oars

men rowing

a man steering

the steering oar

the back of the ship (stern)

✤ How many oars can you see?

✤ Look in books for more pictures of Greek ships. Draw what you think the *Argo* may have looked like.

Comparing your story

✤ Talk about the story with a friend and choose a part to illustrate. Be careful not to look at each other's work until you have finished.

✤ Compare your pictures. What differences can you see? Which details are the same in both pictures?

Prince Siddhartha

In some eastern countries, people follow the teachings of the Buddha. He was a very holy man who lived hundreds of years ago. In the summer, his followers hold a festival called Wesak to celebrate his birth, life and death. This is the story of the Buddha.

A queen of India had a baby son, whose skin was the colour of gold. His father, the king, named him Prince Siddhartha.

The fortune-tellers said that Prince Siddhartha would become either a great king or a holy man. If he was kept safe from all the unhappiness in the world, he would become a king, but if he ever met with pain, sickness and death, then he would become a holy man, and wander the world trying to find an answer to people's suffering.

Now, the Buddha's father wanted his baby son to be a king, so he built a great palace surrounded by beautiful gardens. He gave orders that his son was never to leave the palace and that only those who were young and healthy should be allowed near him. The king's commands were obeyed and all through his childhood, Prince Siddhartha never once saw a man or woman who was old or sick.

Then one day he rode out alone to visit a village nearby because there was to be a festival there. He went without warning and the villagers had no time to prepare for his coming. There, for the first time in his life, Prince Siddhartha came face to face with pain and death, and he was troubled.

He returned to the palace, but he could no longer enjoy his pleasant life. Instead, he thought night and day about what he had seen and struggled to understand why people must suffer.

He left his servants, his jewels and fine clothes and went out into the wilderness to look for an answer. He wandered there for six years, eating little and sleeping less until he came at last to a great fig tree. There he sat, perfectly still, day after day, searching deeper and deeper inside himself to find the answer to the question. Rain lashed him, and the sun burned him but still he sat, thinking. Demons attacked him and hurled thunderstorms at his head but he would not move.

At the end of five weeks, because he had been so strong, heaven rewarded him. A great light shone and understanding came to him. At last he saw the place of suffering in the pattern of life and he knew that, because he understood, he was ready to leave the world behind him and go up into heaven.

But he still wanted to help other people and so he chose to remain on Earth to pass on what he had learned. He spent the rest of his days travelling the world, teaching and praying.

People still follow Prince Siddhartha's teachings today. They call him the Buddha which means 'the bringer of light', and they try to live as he did and to be at peace with each other and with the world.

Prince Siddhartha

Name _____

The story of the Buddha

At Wesak, Buddhists remember the birth, life and death of the Buddha.

✤ Tell his story in pictures and writing.

Perfect peace

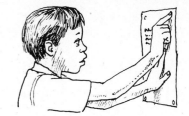

The Buddha gave his followers rules to help them to live peacefully together.

✤ Make up five class rules to make your classroom a peaceful place.

1

2

3

4

5

Name _____

Japanese New Year

In Japan, the people make lucky decorations for New Year. They make them out of pine, bamboo and rope. This story tells why they use rope.

The sun goddess had quarrelled with her brother, the moon. She hid herself in a dark cave and she wouldn't come out. So the sun didn't shine, and day never came. Instead, it was always night.

The gods and goddesses decided that they must do something about it. One by one, they stood outside her cave and tried to coax her to come out; but she wouldn't. She stayed in the dark and it went on being night.

So then they tried to trick her. They gathered outside the cave and danced and sang at the tops of their voices.

The sun goddess could hear them, but she couldn't see what they were doing. She came to the opening of the cave and peeped out. There, in front of her she saw her own reflection.

The gods had secretly climbed up and hung a mirror in the trees. The sight held her quite still for a moment and all the gods sprang forward and hauled her out. As soon as she appeared, the sun leapt into the sky and it was daylight.

Then the gods tied ropes across the entrance to the cave to stop her going back in. From that day forward the sun has always shone, as it should, and the Japanese have always made rope decorations for New Year, just to make sure that the sun goddess never hides again.

New Year customs

Each of these pictures show people celebrating a New Year custom in a different country.

❖ Try to work out which country is which and then find and mark the countries on the map.

❖ Find out more about New Year around the world.

At midnight, the people in this country join hands in a circle and sing a song called 'Auld lang syne'.

Some people in this country gather in Trafalgar Square to see in the New Year.

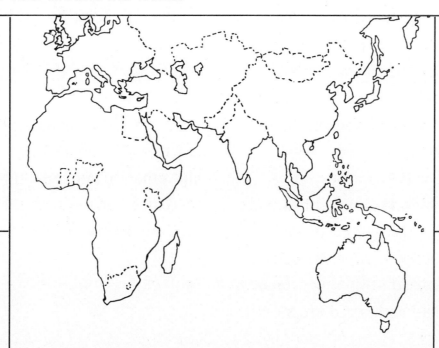

At New Year, they make rope decorations in this country.

In this country they do a lion dance at New Year.

In this country, New Year is called Diwali.

St George and the dragon

St George's Day is 23 April. St George is the patron saint of England and this is one of the traditional stories about him.

There was once a town which was troubled by a dragon. The dragon ate up all the sheep and goats and pigs and cows, and when they had all gone, it started eating people at the rate of one a day. The townsfolk drew lots to decide who went next and one day it was the turn of the king's daughter.

They took her up the hillside and tied her to a rock. Then they left her for the dragon to eat. She was struggling to get free when a young knight came riding up. He was dressed in shining armour and he carried a white shield with a red cross on it. It was St George.

The princess called out for him to run away, but instead, he drew his sword. The dragon charged, breathing fire, and St George attacked. The dragon tried again, and again was driven back. On the third attempt, St George struck it such a mighty blow that all the fight was knocked out of it.

Then he took the princess's belt and tied it around the dragon's neck. The princess led the dragon back into the town and it followed her as good as gold.

So the princess was saved, and the rest of the townspeople too. As for St George, he rode off to find other adventures. But every year, on 23 April, we remember the story of his fight with the dragon.

Name _____

A calendar of special days

♣ Can you find a special day for every month of this year? Here are some to start you off:

- Christmas Day;

- St Valentine's Day;

- Eid-ul-Fitr;

- Chinese New Year;

- May Day;

- your birthday.

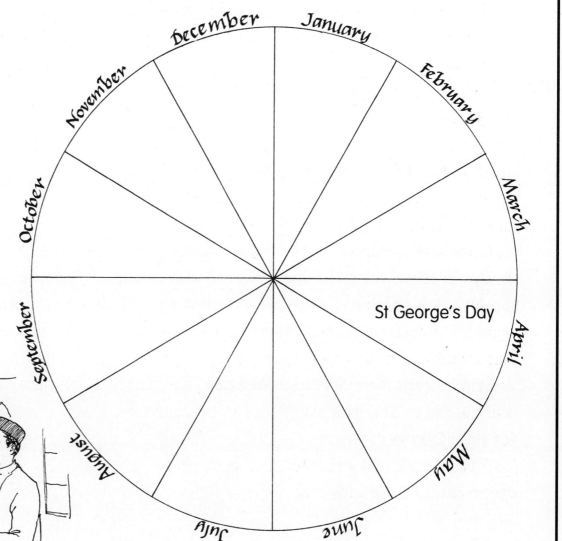

Name _____

St Patrick and the snakes

St Patrick's Day, 17 March, is especially important for the people of Ireland because St Patrick is their patron saint.

St Patrick was born in Wales and when he was a young man he was taken prisoner during a war and carried off to France where he was sold as a slave. He managed to escape and he became a holy man, spending all his time praying and serving God.

One night St Patrick had a dream. He was told in the dream to go to Ireland and teach the Irish people about God. He obeyed the dream and spent the rest of his life in Ireland, building churches and talking about God.

While he was there, St Patrick worked many miracles. The Irish say he got rid of all the snakes in Ireland and that's why there are no snakes there today.

They say that he began by praying very hard that God would send the snakes away, and one by one they all rushed out of their hiding places and flung themselves into the sea until only one was left behind. It was a very big snake and a very old one and pray as St Patrick might, it would not budge.

So then St Patrick made a big wooden box with a tight-fitting lid. He showed it to the snake and said, 'I've made this box for you. Why don't you try it out?'

'No,' said the snake. 'It's too small.'

'It's a perfect fit,' said St Patrick, 'just try it and see.'

'I'm telling you it's far too small,' said the snake. 'I'll show you.'

So it crawled into the box and curled itself up tight. But, as soon as the tip of its tail was in, St Patrick slammed the lid on and threw the box, and the snake, into the sea.

So that was the last snake that ever lived in Ireland.

Now you can believe this tale or not, but the fact of the matter is that you can go from one end of Ireland to the other and not a snake will you find – and that's no story.

St Patrick and the snakes

The Union Jack

The Union Jack is the flag of the United Kingdom. It is made up of three flags: one for England, one for Scotland and one for Ireland.

✤ Using reference books to help you, colour in the flags correctly.

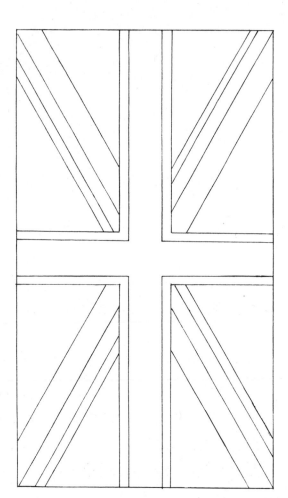

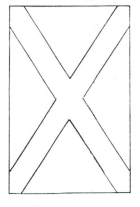

The cross of St Andrew for Scotland.

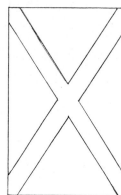

The cross of St Patrick for Ireland.

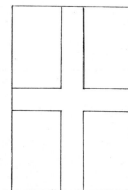

The cross of St George for England.

✤ The flag of which country in the United Kingdom is not included in the Union Jack?

✤ What does this country's flag look like?

Rama and Sita

There was once a king of India who had four sons by different wives. The eldest son was called Rama and everyone knew he would be king when his father died.

However, the king's second wife was jealous of Rama. She wanted her own son to have the crown, and she set out to turn the old king against Rama. Night and day she whispered her lies, poisoning the king's mind until at last he agreed to banish Rama from the kingdom for 14 years.

So Rama, with his wife Sita, left his own land and went out into the dark forest. Years passed and Sita grew more beautiful every day, until one day the king of the demons saw her and wanted her. He kidnapped her by a trick and carried her off to the island of Lanka where he kept her prisoner.

Rama searched for her high and low, but he could not find her. So, he asked for help from the monkeys. The monkeys eventually found her on

the island, but Rama had no way to get across. So the monkeys, by magic, made themselves into a bridge, stretching from the mainland all the way across the sea to Lanka. Rama walked on the monkeys' backs over the sea to Lanka and brought Sita safely home again.

Diwali

Then he and the monkeys attacked the demon king and his army. There was a battle which lasted for ten days and at the end of it the demon king was dead.

By now the time of banishment was up and Rama and Sita came riding out of the dark forest. When the people heard they were coming, they set lamps, or divas, in their windows to light the way. They sang and shouted and cheered as Rama returned to take the throne which his brothers had kept safe for him. From that day to this, people light lamps at the festival of Diwali and remember the happy day when Lord Rama came safely home again.

Storytelling

❖ See if you can tell the story of Rama and Sita to a friend. Use the pictures to help you.

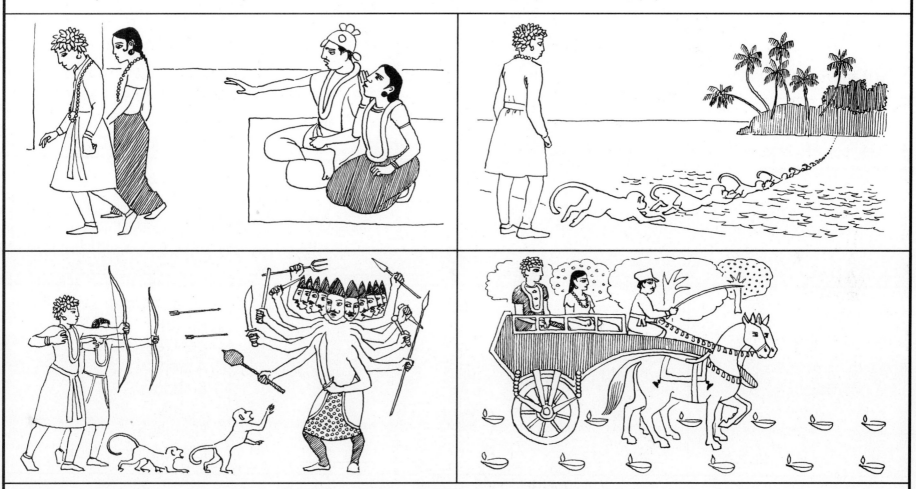

❖ Now write the story of Rama and Sita, or make a play about it. You could plan your ideas on the back of this sheet.

Name _____

Fire symbols

Lighted lamps are a symbol of Diwali.

❖ Here are some more fire symbols. Can you name the special days they celebrate?

❖ Choose the correct day from the list below and write it under its symbol.

_____

_____

_____

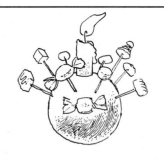

_____

_____

_____

_____

Special days
Easter
Bonfire Night
Advent
Birthdays
Diwali
Hanukah
Chinese New Year

❖ Draw a picture of your favourite fire festival.

The marathon

The Olympic games are held once every four years. Men and women from all over the world meet to take part in races and competitions. One event is called the marathon. It is a very long running race and this is the story of how it first started, thousands of years ago, in Greece.

In those days, Greece was not one big country. Instead it was made up of lots of little cities. One of those cities was called Athens and another was called Sparta.

The king of Persia decided to make war on the Greek cities. He wanted to make them part of his kingdom. So he gathered an enormous army and a great fleet of fighting ships and set off to attack Athens. The army landed near Athens, at a place called Marathon.

When the people of Athens heard that the Persian army was coming, they were very frightened. They sent all their soldiers to Marathon to fight the Persians but they knew that wasn't enough. So they chose their best and fastest runner and told him to run all the way to Sparta to ask for help. When he got there, he found the Spartans busy praying to their gods and they wouldn't come. They said they would send help when they had finished.

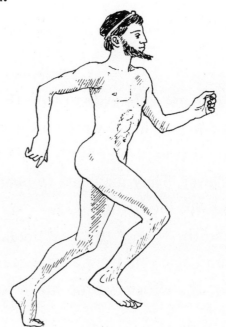

The Olympic Games

So he ran back to Marathon with the bad news that the Athenian soldiers were on their own. The Persian army was very big, but the Athenians were quick and clever. They managed to beat back the Persians and win the battle.

They told the runner to carry the good news to Athens and again he went as fast as he could.

However, the effort was too much for him.

He managed to get there, but when he had delivered his message, he fell down and died.

The long race which is run today is called the marathon because it measures exactly the same distance as the run made from Marathon to Athens (about 26 miles or 42 kilometres). Thousands of years later we still remember the courage of the man who ran the first marathon.

The Greek Olympics

♣ Look up the Ancient Greek Olympics in a reference book and make a list of the different events.

♣ Which sports are shown in the pictures below?

Christmas

 # St Nicholas

The special day of St Nicholas is 6 December. He was a saint who lived a long time ago but we still remember him every Christmas time. This story explains why.

One dark winter's evening, Saint Nicholas was walking through the town when he heard the sound of crying in a house nearby. He tiptoed up to the window and looked in. He saw a bare, cold room with no fire in the grate. Three girls dressed in rags sat at the table, all sobbing as if their hearts would break.

They were poor, hungry and cold, but that wasn't the reason for their tears. They were crying because they had no money to get married.

When St Nicholas heard this, he made up his mind to help them. He went back home and fetched three bags of gold. Then he climbed up on the roof and dropped the bags of gold down the chimney. The girls rushed out to see who had brought the gold, but by the time they got there, St Nicholas was gone.

From that day on, so the story goes, St Nicholas travels out every Christmas Eve, with a big sack of presents, which he drops down the chimneys to make children happy.

In Holland, Saint Nicholas is called *Sinter Klaas*. Dutch settlers took the custom of gifts from Sinter Klaas over to America, where he came to be known as Santa Claus and his visits were believed to be made on Christmas Eve. Whatever his name, people believe that he's still out there on Christmas Eve with his sleigh and his reindeer bringing presents for children.

Stained-glass designs

♣ Design a stained-glass window, showing St Nicholas with his three bags of gold.

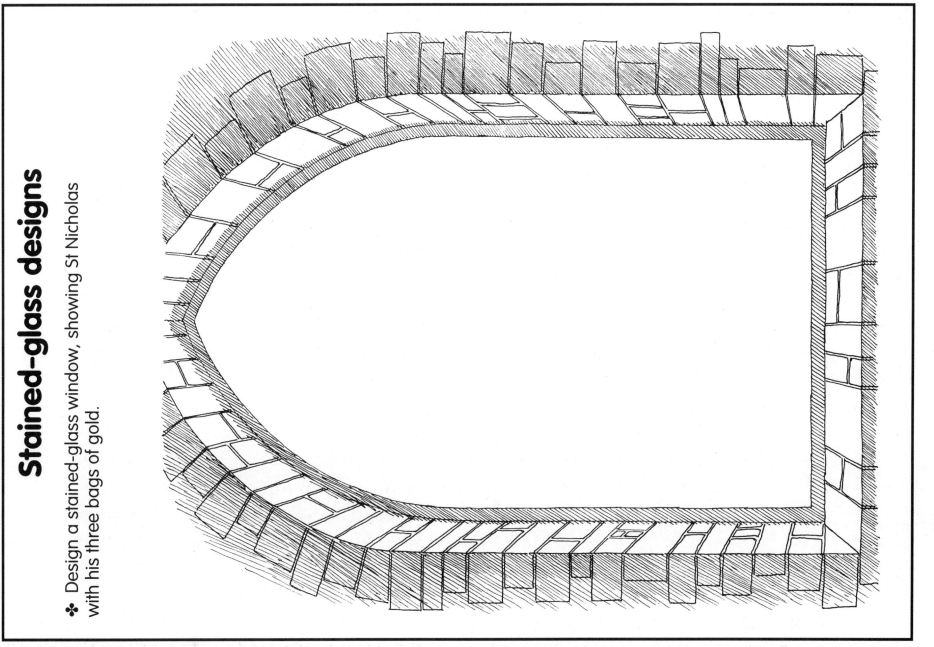

Twelfth Night

La Befana

 On 6 January, 'Twelfth Night', the Christian church remembers the special day when the Three Kings reached Bethlehem and gave their presents to baby Jesus. It is the last of the twelve days of Christmas and it is the time when Christmas decorations are taken down and put away for another year. But Italian children look forward to it because it's the day when La Befana comes and leaves them a stocking full of sweets and nuts to eat. This is her story.

La Befana was a little old lady who lived at the time of the first Christmas. She was cleaning her house one day when she saw a great star shining in the sky and the Three Kings came riding by, with crowns on their heads, carrying gold and frankincense and myrrh.

 She said, 'Where are you going?' and they replied, 'We're following the star. A great king has been born today and the star will guide us to him. We have gifts for him. Come with us and you can bring a present for him too.'

 La Befana shook her head. She said, 'I'm too busy. I've got my house to clean and I can't stop now. I'll wait until you come back and you can tell me where to go.'

So the Three Kings rode off and La Befana finished cleaning her house. Once they had gone, La Befana wished very much that she had gone with them, and that they would not be long in returning.

So she waited, and she waited. Time passed and winter changed to spring, but there was no sign of the Three Kings. Spring turned to summer and still they didn't come. They had had to go home another way and had forgotten all about La Befana.

When autumn drew near, she decided to go looking herself. She filled a sack with nuts and sweets as a present for the baby king and she set off on her own. But it was too late. The star had gone and she never did find him. So she left the sweets and nuts in the stockings of sleeping children and went back home again. From that day to this, every year on Twelfth Night, Italian children find sweets in their stockings. They are left there by La Befana who is still looking for the Christ-child.

Name _____

La Befana

The twelve days of Christmas

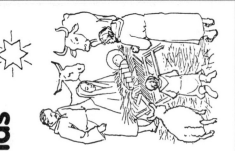

Here are the twelve days of Christmas.

♣ Find out about the special customs which happen on: Boxing Day, New Year's Eve, New Year's Day and Twelfth Night.

♣ Draw something that happens on each special day and in the other boxes draw some of the things that you like to do in the Christmas holidays.

26 December Boxing Day	27 December	28 December
29 December	30 December	31 December New Year's Eve
1 January New Year's Day	2 January	3 January
4 January	5 January	6 January Twelfth Night

Christmas-time traditions

✤ How many Christmas-time traditions can you spot in this picture? Can you put them into the order in which they might occur around Christmas?

✤ Find out how Christmas is celebrated in other countries.

Name _____

Every day is special

Some of these days will be special just for your family. Some are special for other people.

♣ Draw a picture for each day. Then cut them out and sort them into two sets under the correct heading labels.

Special days for my family.		Special days for other people.	
Christmas	**my birthday**	**Diwali**	**a wedding**
Bonfire Night	**New Year's Day**	**an anniversary**	**Choose your own special day to draw.**

Patron saints

St Nicholas
Special day: 6 December
Symbol: three bags
of gold
Patron saint of Russia

St Swithin
Special day: 15 July
Patron saint of weather

St George
Special day: 23 April
Symbol: red cross on a
white background
Patron saint of England

St Christopher
Special day: 25 July
Patron saint of travellers

St Patrick
Special day: 17 March
Symbol: the shamrock
Patron saint of Ireland

St Valentine
Special day: 14 February
Patron saint of love

✤ Match the right beginning and ending:

St George is the patron saint	of travellers.
St Valentine's day is on	the shamrock.
St Christopher is the patron saint	of England.
St Patrick's symbol is	St Swithin's day.
15 July is	St Nicholas.
The patron saint of Russia is	14 February.

✤ Find out about some other saints. For example, who were
St David and St Andrew?

The Pied Piper of Hamelin

There's a town in Germany called Hamelin. This is the story that people tell about it.

Once upon a time there was a plague of rats in Hamelin. There were thousands of them and nothing the townspeople could do would get rid of them. They tried traps and poison and dogs and magic, but still the rats came back bigger and bolder than ever until everyone was in despair.

Then one day a stranger came to town. His clothes were half of red and half of yellow, and he carried a pipe in his hands. He went straight to the Mayor and said, 'What will you give me to get rid of the rats?'

'Anything you like,' said the Mayor. 'As much gold as you can carry! Name your price, sir, and we'll promise to meet it.'

The Pied Piper nodded and put the pipe to his lips. He played a little lilting tune and, as he did so,

out came the rats, pouring from cellars and attics, from doors and windows in a river of whiskers and paws and long twitching tails to dance to his piping. He led them down the main street, through the fields and into the river where they drowned.

The next day the Pied Piper went back to the Mayor. 'I've come for my money,' he said. 'You promised me gold.'

But the Mayor laughed at him, and said, 'That was yesterday. You've rid us of the rats now and we

Name _____

don't need you any more. Be off with you!' And he called for his guards to send the Pied Piper away.

The Pied Piper stood by the Mayor's door. Some of the townspeople went by. He asked them for help, but they only laughed and walked on. So  presently he raised the pipes to his lips again, but this time he played a different tune. It was light and jigging like a dance and tripping and skipping out of the houses came all the children of Hamelin, stepping in time to the music. Off they went, dancing after him, out of the town and up into the mountains.

When the townspeople saw what was happening they came running and called out to the Pied Piper to stop. They offered him gold and land and treasure but he wouldn't listen and the children danced on. They followed him over hill and dale, until a great door opened in the mountainside and in they all went. Then the door swung shut behind them for ever.

For years afterwards the people of Hamelin sat by their lonely fireplaces and cursed the Mayor for his cheating, but it was too late. Neither the Pied Piper, nor the children, were ever seen again.

Name _____

Deep in thought

♣ Can you guess what everyone is thinking?

I'll get rid of the rats for the Mayor because...

I don't care if the Pied Piper gets paid because...

The Pied Piper

A townsman

I won't bother to pay the Pied Piper now because...

I wish we'd paid the Pied Piper because...

The Mayor

A mother

♣ Retell the whole story from the point of view of one of these characters.

Sindbad the sailor

Sindbad the sailor came from Baghdad. He was a great traveller and he had many wonderful adventures. This is part of one of them.

One day, Sindbad and his shipmates landed on an island which was covered with fruit trees. They ate their fill and then Sindbad went to sleep. When he woke up it was nearly dark and there was no sign of the others. He ran back to the shore only to see the ship sailing off without him. He was stranded.

He began to explore the island and found a huge, round, white thing lying on the sand. Then far away he saw a bird of enormous size. He realised that the white thing was its egg and the bird was coming towards it. So he waited till it landed and tied himself to its claw with his turban. The bird lifted him up and carried him away to a deep valley surrounded by mountains.

Sindbad explored the valley. The sides were so steep that there was no way in or out. Its floor was littered with huge diamonds and there were

poisonous snakes everywhere. He found a little cave and spent the night there, but all night long the snakes hissed at him and frightened him until he could scarcely sleep.

In the morning, just as it was getting light, he heard a noise and ran out to see a great piece of raw meat tumbling down the side of the valley. As it rolled, it picked up diamonds from the valley floor. One of the great birds swooped down and picked it up.

Sindbad knew at once what was happening for he had heard of it in stories. The birds were called 'rocs' and the people who lived nearby used them to collect diamonds from the valley. The mountain sides were too steep to climb, so the people threw meat in for the rocs. The birds carried the meat back to their nests to feed their young and the people climbed up to the nests to collect the diamonds which had stuck to the meat.

Sindbad gathered up the diamonds until he had a big bagful. Then he chose the biggest bit of meat and tied himself to it with his turban. He lay quite still until a roc swooped down on to the meat and carried him up to its nest.

He found the diamond gatherers hiding around the rocs' nests and, with their help, he escaped to safety. He returned to Baghdad laden with treasure, which he shared with the poor. He bought himself a palace and lived there in splendour. However, what became of his crew, the story does not tell.

Famous sailors

Sindbad the sailor was not a real person. He was imaginary.
Here are some more famous sailors.

✤ Can you guess who was real and who was imaginary?
Use reference books to check.

Christopher Columbus   **Odysseus**   **Francis Drake**   **Long John Silver**   **Anne Bonny**   **Captain Cook**

♣ Find out more about one of them and jot some notes down in the box below.

Rip Van Winkle

Rip Van Winkle lived in America about 200 years ago. He was an easy-going man who liked a drink and a song and a bit of a party, but his wife was always cross and nagged him from morning until night.

One fine morning, his wife had gone to market and Rip Van Winkle saw the chance of a day's freedom. He whistled to his dog, took his gun and went off hunting on the Catskill Mountains.

He'd climbed a long way and he was just catching his breath when he heard the sound of a fiddle. He moved towards it and came upon a group of men and women dressed in old-fashioned clothes, eating and drinking and playing at ninepins.

Now Rip Van Winkle liked the look of this, so he moved closer and joined in the game. They were all taking swigs from a big black bottle and Rip Van Winkle drank some too. Then he danced with some of the ladies, and had another game of ninepins and, all of a sudden, what with the drink and the dancing and the long climb he felt so sleepy that he couldn't keep his eyes open. He crept into a cave nearby and went fast asleep.

When he woke up, it was getting dark and he was stiff and shivering. There was no sign of the strange people, and his dog had vanished. He was all alone on the mountainside. His gun lay beside him, but it was brown with rust and he ached as if he'd slept for 100 years. He hurried down the hillside, afraid that his wife would scold him for coming home so late.

However, when he reached his house, it was quite changed. A stranger was working in his garden and the young apple trees had grown as tall as the rooftop. He wandered the streets, but they had changed too and he didn't know a living soul. The passers-by stared at him and pointed at his long grey beard until at last he cried, 'Is there no one who knows me? I'm Rip Van Winkle.'

Then an old man said, 'Rip Van Winkle? But he went missing in the Catskill Mountains, and that was 100 years ago.'

And so it was that Rip Van Winkle learned that he had slept 100 years away. When he went to sleep, America was ruled by King George III of England. When he awoke, he was a free citizen of the United States of America. He had lost his wife, his family and everything he ever knew. Although he searched the Catskill Mountains for many a long day, he could find no trace of the cave. And as for the men and women who played at ninepins, he never saw them again.

Rip Van Winkle

Name _____

100 years on

❖ Imagine you have gone to sleep for 100 years. What does the world look like when you wake up?

❖ Draw a picture of what you see when you wake up, and write a story about what happens to you.

Newfangled machines

❖ Imagine you have just met Rip Van Winkle. Can you explain to him what these machines do?

❖ What would he have used in his time?

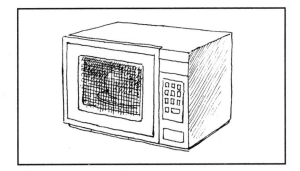

Used for: _____
Rip Van Winkle would have used:

_____

Used for: _____
Rip Van Winkle would have used:

_____

Used for: _____
Rip Van Winkle would have used:

_____

Used for: _____
Rip Van Winkle would have used:

_____

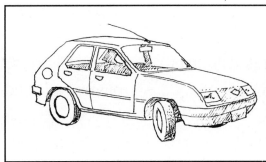

Used for: _____
Rip Van Winkle would have used:

_____

Used for: _____
Rip Van Winkle would have used:

_____

Anansi looks for a wife

In Africa there are many stories about Anansi, a creature who is half man and half spider. He is the smallest creature in the jungle, but he is also the cleverest and usually gets his own way, as this story shows.

Anansi was lonely living on his own. He was tired of cooking his own food and cleaning his own hut, so he decided to go looking for a wife.

He walked and walked until he was quite tired out and then he sat down to rest under a fig tree. He was just dropping off to sleep when he saw a beautiful woman coming towards him. She was tall and shining and she swayed like a dancer. A light came from her face and her hair was the colour of flames. It was Fire and when Anansi saw her, he knew he must have her for his wife.

Anansi clapped his hands and stamped his feet and danced for her. Fire drew closer and he sang and drummed and talked to her as only Anansi can talk. He offered her everything he owned in the world if only she would come and visit him.

At last Fire nodded, smiling, and said, 'Make me a trail and I will come. I will visit you tomorrow.' And with that, she was gone.

Anansi snatched up a brush and began to sweep a trail. He made it smooth and wide. Then he covered it with dry sticks and twigs to feed Fire on her journey. It took him all day and all night and he was just approaching his own house when he saw Fire coming, from far away across the hills. He could see her bright flames dancing and the crackle of twigs sounded like laughter.

Anansi brushed harder than ever. The trail was almost complete and Fire was coming very fast. She grew taller with every step and, as she came, she swallowed up whole trees. Anansi felt a little afraid.

By now her flames almost touched the sky and she roared like a lion. She raced along his trail faster than he could lay it.

'Where is your house, Anansi?' cried Fire, in a voice like thunder.

'Over here,' said Anansi and he began to sweep as hard as he could go. But he swept the trail away from his own house and towards the river.

Fire raced after him, faster and faster. She didn't look where she was going. She didn't see Anansi jump aside. She raced straight into the river and went out and the house was safe. So Anansi didn't find a wife, but he had learned how to handle fire and that was a lesson he remembered for the rest of his life.

Anansi looks for a wife

Name _____

Fire poems

✤ Think of some words to describe fire, and write them in the flames below.

✤ Now use your word list to help you to write a fire poem for Anansi.

The jackdaw of Rheims

A long time ago, in the city of Rheims, there lived a cardinal who kept a jackdaw as a pet. A cardinal is a very important man in the Church indeed and this one lived in a fine palace. He sat on a velvet throne and so did the jackdaw, for it was always at his side.

The cardinal was at dinner one night, dressed in silks and satins. He wore a great ring on his finger and a cross of gold around his neck. The table cloth was of the finest linen and the plates were made of gold, but the cardinal ate with his fingers, because in those days nobody had invented forks.

So after he had finished, his servants brought water for him to wash his hands and he took off the ring and dipped his fingers in the bowl. When he turned to pick up the ring, it had vanished.

The cardinal called for his servants and he called for his guards. They searched the palace from top to bottom, but there was no sign of the ring. Then the cardinal called for the thief to come forward, but nobody stirred.

So, he called for his Bible and he laid a solemn curse on whoever had stolen the ring. He cursed that thief waking and sleeping, eating and drinking and in whatever he did. Then he sat back and waited.

Nothing happened. The ring didn't turn up and everybody in the palace stayed well and strong. It was a complete mystery.

Next day, the jackdaw appeared. It was a changed creature. It had lost half its feathers and the others were crumpled and dull. It shivered miserably and it hardly had the strength to croak. As soon as he saw it, the cardinal knew that his curse had found the guilty one. He had found his thief.

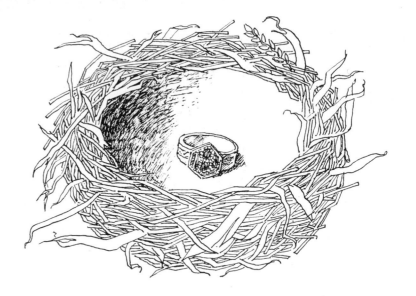

The servants went to the jackdaw's nest and found the ring half hidden under the straw. The cardinal put it back on his finger and made haste to take off his great curse. Straightaway the jackdaw began to perk up again. Its feathers grew glossy and its eyes became bright.

From that day on, it never stole again. It stayed with the cardinal until it died and it was the best behaved jackdaw in Rheims.

Good table manners

Here are some table manners dating from the cardinal's time.

Wash your hands before you eat, so that those who dip their fingers in the same dish, know you have cleaned them.

Don't pick your nose or your teeth at the table.

Don't lean on the table.

Don't scratch. If you have an itch use a bit of cloth so that your hands stay clean.

Wipe your mouth before you drink.

Keep your own knife sharp.

It is rude to poke around the dish, looking for the best bit of meat.

❖ Which of these rules do we follow today?

❖ Make a list of table manners for today.

Black duck's children

This is a story from Australia. Australia is an island and it has its own special plants and animals which are quite different from those of other countries. One very strange creature is the duck-billed platypus. It lays eggs like a bird, but it has fur like a mammal. Its feet are webbed, and it has a long leathery beak. This story explains where it came from.

Long long ago, in Dreamtime, when all the animals and birds were made, there was a little black duck who lived on a lake along with many others of her tribe. She ate and slept and swam with them and she never strayed too far from the flock for fear of enemies who might catch and kill her.

One day she found a patch of sweet young grass on the water's edge and as she ate she moved further from the lake until she had lost sight of all the others and she was quite alone.

A water rat pounced on her and carried her off to his burrow on the lakeside to be his wife. The little duck didn't want to marry him, but he kept her prisoner in the burrow and guarded her night and day, in case she tried to escape.

The black duck saw she had no chance of getting away, so she pretended to give in. She told the water rat that she was happy to be his wife and he, believing her, began to guard her less closely.

One night when the water rat fell asleep the duck saw her chance. She crept out of the burrow and ran away home to her own people, and very glad she was to be free.

When the time came for nest-making, and the other ducks laid eight or ten eggs, she had only two. When these two hatched they were odd little creatures, half rat and half duck. For they had four feet like a rat, but these feet were webbed like a duck's. They had rat's fur, but a duck's beak, and all in all they were such an odd mixture that the duck tribe drove them and their mother away.

So the little family wandered far into the mountains until they came to a sheltered pool and there she brought them up. In time the two strange children had children of their own and then grandchildren, until there was a whole tribe of them living in the mountains. There they still live today, as the creature we call the duck-billed platypus.

Black duck's children

Animal magic

Long ago, before people could read and write, they started to wonder how the world began. They made up stories to explain where the first birds and animals came from. These stories are called myths.

♣ Choose one of these animals below. Make up your own story to explain where it came from, and why it looks like it does. Or choose your own animal to write about.

elephant

snake

jellyfish

dachshund (sausage dog)

Name _____

Australian originals

♣ Find the names of these Australian creatures in this word search puzzle:

b	k	a	n	g	a	r	o	o	c	d
e	o	f	o	g	n	i	d	c	g	h
k	o	a	l	a	b	e	a	r	i	j
m	k	n	p	o	p	l	q	o	r	s
w	a	l	l	a	b	y	t	c	u	v
w	b	t	a	x	y	r	z	o	a	b
c	u	a	t	d	e	e	u	d	f	g
h	r	b	y	i	j	b	m	i	k	l
m	r	m	p	n	o	i	e	l	p	q
r	a	o	u	s	t	r	u	e	v	w
x	y	w	s	z	a	d	b	c	d	e

kangaroo

lyre bird

emu

koala bear

dingo

wombat

platypus

crocodile

kookaburra

wallaby

Mesopotamia

Gilgamesh

Thousands and thousands of years ago, when history first began, there was a kingdom called Mesopotamia which lay between two rivers. Its chief town was called Babylon, and the Babylonians were the first people ever to invent writing. They made marks with wedge-shaped sticks on tablets of soft clay. The sun baked the clay dry and the writing lasted for ever. We still have some of those tablets and one of them tells a story. It's possibly the oldest story in the world and it's the legend of Gilgamesh.

Gilgamesh was a mighty hero. He was one part man and two parts god, so he was braver and stronger than any man alive. Gilgamesh fought with the king of the forest, who had the head of a monster, and he wrestled with a magical bull. And towards the end of his life, he went down into the Underworld to find out the secret of everlasting life. It happened like this.

Night after night Gilgamesh was troubled with dreams of death. At last he decided to ask for help from the wisest man in the world. He was called Uta-Napishtim, and he lived deep in the Underworld where no mortal could go.

Gilgamesh travelled down into the roots of a mountain, which was guarded by scorpion men. A deep, dark tunnel led into the earth. He walked through the blackness for a day and a night and, at the end of that time, he came to a wonderful garden beside a sea. The trees were full of jewelled fruit and the ground was scattered with precious stones.

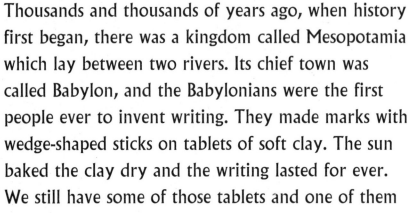

Gilgamesh met a boatman in the garden who told him how to find Uta-Napishtim. He had to pole himself in a boat across the sea, the Water of Death, but he must not touch the water. The boatman helped Gilgamesh to cross the sea and he came at last to the wise man's house, but Uta-Napishtim would not help him. He said the secret was not his to give. Gilgamesh was going sadly away when Uta-Napishtim's wife took pity on him and whispered a secret. At the bottom of the Water of Death, she said, there grew a certain type of plant which made old men young again.

So Gilgamesh tied stones to his feet and plunged to the bottom of the sea. The Water of Death closed round him, but he found the plant and, as he touched it, life returned to him again. He rose to the surface with the plant in his hand, but, just as he was going to eat it, a snake came slithering by and carried it away. So Gilgamesh returned to the land of the living without the secret.

And that's why, so the Babylonians said, from that day onwards, snakes, which had eaten the plant of life, lived for ever. But all people died, whether kings or beggars, because Gilgamesh failed in his quest.

All at once

The legend of Gilgamesh was first written down 2,000 years before the birth of Christ. Here are some others things which were going on at the time.

♣ In each box, draw a small picture of the event and colour it in.

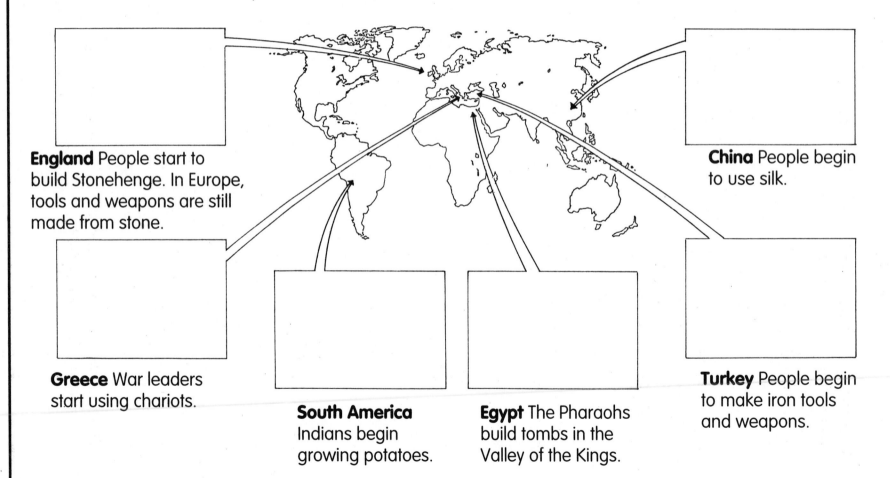

England People start to build Stonehenge. In Europe, tools and weapons are still made from stone.

China People begin to use silk.

Greece War leaders start using chariots.

South America Indians begin growing potatoes.

Egypt The Pharaohs build tombs in the Valley of the Kings.

Turkey People begin to make iron tools and weapons.

Beginning to write

When the story of Gilgamesh was first told, the people of Mesopotamia used symbols for their writing.

For example: ox =

By the time the story was written down, they were using shapes made up of a series of small lines. This writing is called 'cuneiform'.

For example: ox =

♣ Below are some words written in symbols and in cuneiform. Can you match them up? One has been done for you.

symbols

cuneiform

sky

day

water

to eat

to go

♣ What do you think the symbols might have looked like for: 'mountain' and 'to be furious'?

Name _____

General sheet

A special world

❖ Use an atlas to find the places listed below.

❖ Now using the key, mark them on the map opposite.

France	**F**
Germany	**G**
Arabia	**A**
North America	**NA**
Africa	**Af**
Australia	**Au**
United Kingdom	**UK**

❖ Which country does your story come from?